If You Were an ILLUSTRATOR

by Anne Sibley O'Brien
illustrated by Nick Backes

Harcourt

Orlando   Boston   Dallas   Chicago   San Diego

Visit *The Learning Site!*

www.harcourtschool.com

The Job of Illustrating

Do you like to draw? Do you think it would be fun to get paid to draw pictures that appear in books? That's the job of a children's book illustrator.

Imagine that you were to become an illustrator. What skills would you need for the job? It would help if you had been drawing since you were a child, so you had lots of practice. Perhaps a parent or a teacher encouraged you, so you kept drawing even when it got difficult. Many people who become illustrators study art in college, though that's not absolutely necessary. If you love to read, that's an advantage also, because you would already know a lot about books.

To illustrate children's books, you don't go to an office and apply for a job. Instead, you put together your best pictures in a big flat case called a *portfolio*. Then you call a publishing company and ask if you can come in to show your portfolio to an *art director*. The art director is the person who is in charge of book illustrations at the publishing company.

You can also mail samples of your work to art directors. You can make color photocopies of your favorite pictures and send them to publishing companies all over the country. When an art director likes your pictures, he or she will keep them on file and start looking for a story that is right for your illustration style—or styles, if you have more than one.

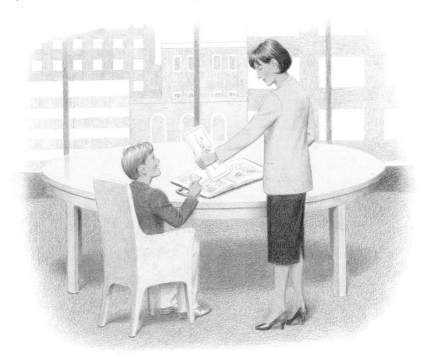

Getting a Book to Illustrate

One day you will get a phone call from an art director who will say, "I have a book for you to illustrate! I think it's perfect for you. I will send the story in the mail."

What an exciting conversation! Now you watch the mail eagerly, waiting for the story to arrive. On the day it comes, you open the envelope and begin reading the story for the first time. The story is typed on ordinary white paper and is called a *manuscript.*

As soon as you've read the manuscript, you call the art director on the phone. "I love the story!" you say. "I'm happy to illustrate it. Thank you so much for thinking of me."

The Contract

Now the publishing company will send you a *contract*, which is a written agreement of the promises that you and the publisher are making. The contract says that you promise to illustrate the story by a certain date, perhaps a year from now. The publisher promises to pay you a certain amount of money for doing the job. The publisher will give you half of the money right away so you have some income while you're working. You will get the other half when you turn in the final illustrations. After reading the contract carefully, you sign it and return it to the publisher.

Now you are ready to start illustrating!

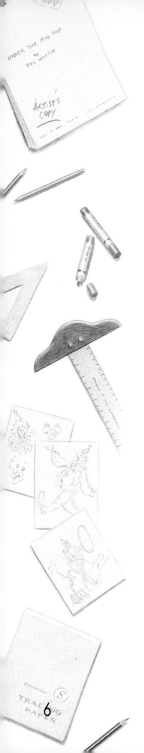

Beginning the Roughs

Just as a writer creates rough drafts before making a final story, an illustrator goes through a long process–weeks or months–of thinking about and creating rough illustrations before painting the final pictures. This is the most important part of the illustration process, because it is where you make most of your decisions about how your book will look.

First you read the manuscript again and again. You take your time to let the story settle in your mind, to give your imagination time to work. What images come into your mind's eye?

There is a lot to think about! What do you think the main characters should look like? How do you see the landscape or setting? If you have more than one style, which of them do you think would fit the story best? What kind of colors would suit the story: light pastel colors; strong, bright primary colors; or rich, dark colors? Will your illustrations go in a book that is little or big? Will the book be a tall rectangle or a small square?

Many illustrators begin by making a series of tiny rough sketches, called *thumbnails* because they are so small. Making thumbnails is like taking notes on your original ideas for the pictures you want to draw. You can sketch them very quickly and not worry about what they look like, because no one will see them but you.

The next step is to decide how to divide the manuscript. The illustrator is often the one who decides which words will go on which page. You read the manuscript— again!—and begin to decide what you want to illustrate.

Each time you have an idea for a picture, you mark the section of the manu- script that goes with that picture and number the page it will be on. Most picture books have thirty-two pages, and there are usually one or two pictures for every two pages facing each other, called a *spread*. Some pages are needed for the title and other information at the beginning of the book. This leaves about twenty-eight pages, or fourteen spreads, so you need to imag- ine between fourteen and twenty-eight pictures.

7

STORY BOARD

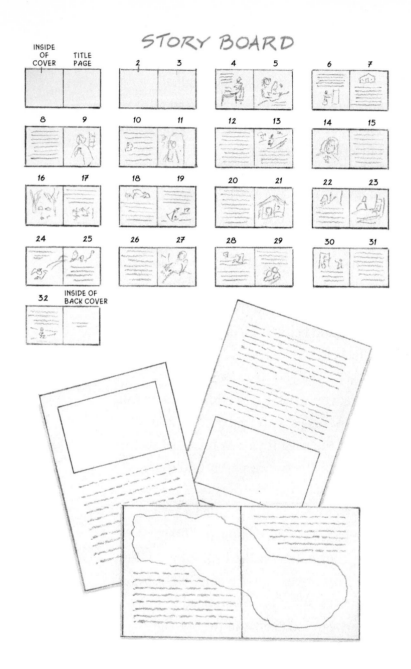

The Storyboard

Once the manuscript is divided, you are ready to make a *storyboard*. A storyboard is a plan for the whole book, like a map that is all on one page. You draw little boxes, one for every page in the book, and number them 1 to 32. Then, following the markings you made on the manuscript and the images from your thumbnail sketches, you make a drawing of each picture idea for each spread. This is the rough stage, so the pictures are still quite small and quick. You don't want to take a lot of time to draw carefully and put in a lot of detail, because you will probably be making many changes.

The most important function of a storyboard is to help you figure out how the words and pictures fit together on each spread. There are many choices. You could put all the words on one page with a picture on the other page. The words could run along the top of both pages with the pictures below. They could appear on the bottom of the pages with the pictures above. You can also combine any of these plans and put words on the bottom on one page, words on top on the other, and a picture going diagonally across the spread. As the illustrator, you try to make the best choices for your book and your style.

The Dummy

The next step is to make a practice book, which has a funny name—a *dummy*! It's called a dummy because it's a model, not the real thing. To make the dummy, you take eight pieces of paper, fold them in half and fasten them with staples. Then you cut the folded papers to be the same size you planned for the book. Number the pages from 1 to 32.

Then you take a copy of the manuscript and cut it up into the sections of words you marked. Using your storyboard as a guide, you glue each block of words onto the correct page on your dummy.

Now you sketch the images that go with each part of the story, just as you planned on your storyboard. Although these are still rough sketches, you can begin to fill them out with more detail to get a sense of what the picture will look like on the page.

Once you have a completed dummy, you should spend some time with it. Read through the story again and again, looking carefully at the pictures and words together. Will the pictures make the reader excited to read the story? Usually you will find quite a number of things you want to change. It doesn't mean that you have made any mistakes, just that you can think of an even better way to illustrate the story. You want the reader to turn the pages and study every picture you drew.

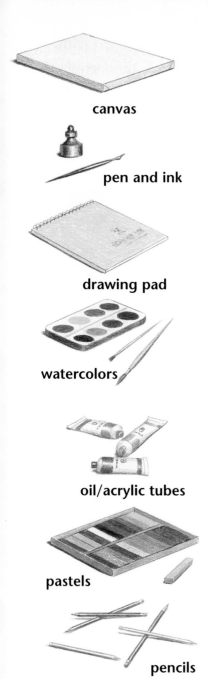

canvas

pen and ink

drawing pad

watercolors

oil/acrylic tubes

pastels

pencils

The Final Paintings

When you are satisfied with your dummy, you send it to the art director. The art director may make a few suggestions for improvements. He or she may also want to see a cover sketch. When you've made all the changes to the dummy, you're ready to begin the final illustrations.

If you and your art director haven't already discussed what *medium* you will use to make the pictures, now is the time! Different kinds of drawing and painting materials are called mediums. Will you use watercolors? Charcoal? Oil paint? Pastels? You'll want to choose a medium that works well for you as an artist and also works well for the story.

Following the plan in your dummy, you make a final sketch of one of the illustrations. You can use tracing paper to change the drawing over and over again until you are satisfied.

Next you'll need to transfer the final drawing from the tracing paper to the final paper you're going to paint on. One way to do this is to turn the tracing paper over and copy the lines exactly on the back side. Flip the tracing paper back over and tape it down to the final paper. Using a metal spoon, scrape carefully and firmly over all the lines until they are transferred to the final paper.

Lift up the tracing paper and you should have a clean, light pencil line directly on the final paper. You can use it as a guide to paint the final illustration.

Creating the finals is a matter of putting together all the work you've done in the roughs. Most of the important decisions have been made. You know what you're drawing, what words each picture will go with, and where the art will appear on the page. You've got the lines of the drawing to follow. Perhaps you even did some color roughs to decide which colors to use. Now you have to make the clearest, most detailed, best image you can, based on these decisions.

Even with all those decisions made, creating the finals usually takes months. It's important to take your time and do your very best work, because once it's printed in a book, you can't change it! Your art director may ask to see one final illustration before you complete the rest.

Months later, when all of your final illustrations are completed, you pack them up carefully and mail them to the publisher. You're done! It's good to take a break and have a little celebration.

It's also good to begin thinking about your next project, because it will take a long, long time for the illustrations you just finished to be printed in the book. It can take as little as six months or as long as two or three years to see a copy of your published book!

One day, though, you'll get a package in the mail from your publisher.

Finally, the Book

With your heart beating fast, you'll open the package in a hurry. Inside will be a brand-new book. There on the cover will be an illustration that you created in your studio! Next to the author's name you will read the words that say, "Illustrated by..." and there will be your name!

Opening the book, you'll look at the pictures that you made, and you'll know that very soon this book will be found in libraries and bookstores all over the country. Children will come into a library or store, and they will see your wonderful illustration on the cover. They'll reach out for the book with both hands, open it, and begin to read.

Imagine...

This month's destination:

Exciting ORLANDO, FLORIDA!

Are you the lucky person who will win a free trip to Orlando? Imagine how much fun it would be to visit Walt Disney World**, Universal Studios**, Cape Canaveral and the other sights and attractions in this area! The Next page contains tow Official Entry Coupons, as does each of the other books you received this shipment. Complete and return *all* the entry coupons—**the more times you enter, the better your chances of winning!**

Then keep your fingers crossed, because you'll find out by October 15, 1995 if you're the winner! If you are, here's what you'll get:

- Round-trip airfare for two to Orlando!
- 4 days/3 nights at a first-class resort hotel!
- $500.00 pocket money for meals and sightseeing!

Remember: The more times you enter, the better your chances of winning!*

*NO PURCHASE OR OBLIGATION TO CONTINUE BEING A SUBSCRIBER NECESSARY TO ENTER. SEE BACK PAGE FOR ALTERNATIVE MEANS OF ENTRY AND RULES.

**THE PROPRIETORS OF THE TRADEMARKS ARE NOT ASSOCIATED WITH THIS PROMOTION.

VOR KAL

FLYAWAY VACATION
SWEEPSTAKES
OFFICIAL ENTRY COUPON

This entry must be received by: SEPTEMBER 30, 1995
This month's winner will be notified by: OCTOBER 15, 1995
Trip must be taken between: NOVEMBER 30, 1995-NOVEMBER 30, 1996

YES, I want to win the vacation for two to Orlando, Florida. I understand the prize includes round-trip airfare, first-class hotel and $500.00 spending money. Please let me know if I'm the winner!

Name_____

Address _____ Apt. _____

City   State/Prov.   Zip/Postal Code

Account #_____

Return entry with Invoice in reply envelope.

© 1995 HARLEQUIN ENTERPRISES LTD.   COR KAL

FLYAWAY VACATION
SWEEPSTAKES
OFFICIAL ENTRY COUPON

This entry must be received by: SEPTEMBER 30, 1995
This month's winner will be notified by: OCTOBER 15, 1995
Trip must be taken between: NOVEMBER 30, 1995-NOVEMBER 30, 1996

YES, I want to win the vacation for two to Orlando, Florida. I understand the prize includes round-trip airfare, first-class hotel and $500.00 spending money. Please let me know if I'm the winner!

Name_____

Address _____ Apt. _____

City   State/Prov.   Zip/Postal Code

Account #_____

Return entry with Invoice in reply envelope.

© 1995 HARLEQUIN ENTERPRISES LTD.   COR KAL

Dear Reader,

When my editor at Temptation first approached me about writing three interlocking stories for the Bachelor Arms series, my first thought was *roommates!* Fortunately, it didn't take me long to realize that having three adult men living in one apartment wasn't going to work. It would be way too crowded for one thing, and how would they carry on their romances if two other guys were always hanging around? Still, the idea wouldn't let go and I began mentally playing that old writer's game *What if?* What if the three men had been roommates in the past? And what if something had happened that had changed their lives forever? Ah, now *there* was an idea rife with dramatic possibilities!

Writing *Seduced and Betrayed* for the Bachelor Arms series was, to coin an old phrase, a real blast from the past. I went through picture albums to remind myself of what we were all wearing when Zeke Blackstone and Ariel Cameron first met. (What was I thinking of when I bought those psychedelic hip-hugger bell-bottoms?) I listened to *Billboard*'s top-ten hits of the era while I wrote, albeit at much lower decibels than the first time around. I even lit a stick of patchouli incense to set the proper mood.

The real fun came, though, in dealing with Zeke and Ariel's present. How were they going to get past the misunderstandings and betrayals of the past to take advantage of the second chance life had offered? I hope you like the way I worked it out for them.

Next month, read my last book in the series, *Passion and Scandal,* to find out what really happened that fateful night in 1970 that changed so many lives. I love to hear from readers, so please write.

Sincerely,

Candace Schuler

c/o Harlequin Temptation
225 Duncan Mill Road
Don Mills, Ontario M3B 3K9
Canada

BACHELOR ARMS

Come live and love in L.A. with the tenants of Bachelor Arms

Bachelor Arms is a trendy apartment building with some very colorful tenants. Meet three confirmed bachelors who are determined to stay single until three very special women turn their lives upside down; college friends who reunite to plan a wedding; a cynical and sexy lawyer; a director who's renowned for his hedonistic life-style and many more…including one very mysterious and legendary tenant. And while everyone tries to ignore the legend, every once in a while something strange happens….

Each of these fascinating people has a tale of success or failure, love or heartbreak. But their stories don't stay a secret for long in the hallways of Bachelor Arms.

Bachelor Arms is a captivating place, home to an eclectic group of neighbors. All of them have one thing in common, though—the feeling of community that is very much a part of living at Bachelor Arms.

BACHELOR ARMS

THE TENANTS OF BACHELOR ARMS

Ken Amberson: The odd superintendent who knows more than he admits about the legend of Bachelor Arms.

Zeke Blackstone: The Hollywood director and ladies' man once shared 1G with Jack and Ethan in their bachelor days.

Ariel Cameron: Zeke was the love of her life—until his betrayal. Now this gorgeous model/actress is wary of seduction—and Zeke.

Eddie Cassidy: Local bartender at Flynn's next door. He's looking for his big break as a screenwriter.

Jill Foyle: This sexy, recently divorced interior designer moved to L.A. to begin a new life.

Natasha Kuryan: This elderly Russian-born femme fatale was a makeup artist to the stars of yesterday.

Bobbie-Sue O'Hara: She works as an actress and waitress but knows that real power lies on the other side of the camera.

Ethan Roberts: Former roommate of Zeke and Jack, this ex-soap star is preparing for his biggest role yet—public office.

Eric Shannon: The aspiring screenwriter's tragic suicide affected the lives of so many people at the B.A.

Faith Shannon: A sweet Georgia peach, now married to Jack and attending med school.

Jack Shannon: The cynical reporter always blamed himself for his brother Eric's mysterious death, but was redeemed by the love of a good woman.

Theodore "Teddy" Smith: The resident Lothario—any new female in the building puts a sparkle in his eye.

Candace Schuler
SEDUCED AND BETRAYED

Harlequin Books

TORONTO • NEW YORK • LONDON
AMSTERDAM • PARIS • SYDNEY • HAMBURG
STOCKHOLM • ATHENS • TOKYO • MILAN
MADRID • WARSAW • BUDAPEST • AUCKLAND

For Kimberly Kaila,

a daughter of the heart

ISBN 0-373-25653-1

SEDUCED AND BETRAYED

Prologue

Los Angeles—1970

ARIEL COULD HEAR the muted thump of rock music as she approached the courtyard of the Bachelor Arms apartment building. The sound rolled through the fanciful wrought iron bars in hard, pulsing waves, throbbing through the warm night air like a heartbeat. It was primitive and wild, echoing the rapid pounding of the blood through her veins. She hesitated a moment, gathering her courage and resolve, and then pushed the gate open and slipped inside. Moving quickly, almost running, she hurried across the shadowed courtyard, skirting the couple making out on the chaise longue and the young man passed out cold on the concrete.

The music became louder as she pushed open the door to the downstairs hallway, the pulsing rhythm evolving into the recognizable lyrics of Cream's hard-driving "Sunshine Of Your Love." Ariel could hear bursts of laughter now too, and smell the faint, distinctively sweet scents of marijuana and patchouli oil as she followed the music down the hall to apartment 1-G.

The door was wide open, inviting in any and all passersby. Ariel's courage faltered for a moment. This kind of party wasn't her scene. The music blaring out into

the hall was too loud; the combined scents of marijuana and incense were nauseating; and the two people leaning against the open door, groping each other
under their clothes, were shocking. And disgusting.
And just a little bit frightening.

She didn't want to go in.

But she had to find Zeke. Once she'd found him, once
she'd explained and apologized, everything would be
all right.

Cautiously, her lower lip caught in her teeth, her eyes
modestly averted, she flattened herself against the
doorjamb to squeeze by the oblivious couple.

"Hey, watch it," one of them yelped as she inadvertently jostled the pair.

"Sorry," Ariel mumbled and pressed her spine closer
to the wall. "I'm sorry. I need to get by."

"Yeah, well, jeez, you coulda just asked," the male
half of the couple complained.

"Sorry," Ariel said again and tried to inch by them.

"Hey, I know you." The girl straightened away from
her partner, inadvertently blocking Ariel's way even
more. "You're Ariel Cameron. Hey, babe." She nudged
her boyfriend. "It's Ariel Cameron. You know, she
plays Chrissy Fortune on *Family Fortune*. That's my
favorite TV show," she said to Ariel.

Ariel shook her head as she pushed on by them. "I'm
not her," she said, and ran down the hall.

There were twenty or so people jammed into the living room. About half of them were crowded onto the
vinyl beanbag chairs and the madras-draped sofa or
just sitting on the floor, drinking wine, passing a joint
around and grooving to the music. The others were
standing around in small groups talking and flirting,
using exaggerated facial expressions and lots of pan-

tomime as they tried to make themselves understood. A slender redheaded girl in a tie-dyed gauze caftan and a leather headband was dancing by herself, her expression vacant as she undulated to the tune of "Crimson and Clover" now blaring from the oversize speakers. But Ariel didn't see Zeke anywhere. Or anyone else she recognized, for that matter.

She leaned down, putting her lips close to the ear of the nearest person. "Have you seen Zeke?" she shouted, trying to make herself heard above the music. "Zeke Blackstone?"

The young man shook his head and offered her a hit of his joint in lieu of the information she'd asked for.

"No, thank you," Ariel said. "I'm looking for Zeke. Zeke Blackstone. He lives here. Have you seen him?"

"Try the kitchen."

Zeke wasn't in the kitchen, either, but one of his roommates was.

"Oh, Ethan, thank goodness," Ariel said, relieved to see someone she knew, even if it was someone she wasn't particularly fond of. "Have you seen Zeke anywhere?"

"He was around here a while ago." Ethan tipped a beer to his lips. "He was looking pretty bummed, too," he said, and smiled at her. "You guys have a fight?"

"No, not a fight, exactly," she lied, not liking Ethan's smile, or the way he looked at her. "I just need to see him. Do you know where he is?"

"He said something about the music giving him a headache." Ethan shrugged. "I think he went to bed." His smile changed into a smirk. "I'm sure you know where his room is."

Ariel whirled away, setting the strands of the beaded curtain that hung in the doorway swaying and clicking against each other as she passed through them.

The door to Zeke's room was closed and there was no light showing around its edges. Ariel put her hand on the doorknob and turned it slowly. "Zeke?" she said softly as she eased into the darkened room and closed the door behind her. "Zeke, are you asleep?"

Apparently, he was. Although how anyone could sleep with the raucous party going on in the next room was a complete mystery to her. She tiptoed toward his bed, her steps guided by memory and the dim moonlight shining in through the single, curtainless window.

"Zeke?" She bent over the bed and reached out to touch the lump under the covers. "Zeke, I—"

"What?" a female voice mumbled sleepily. "What's the matter?"

Ariel snatched her hand back with a muffled shriek. "I'm sorry. I was looking for Zeke Blackstone." she said, backing away from the bed as she spoke. If another pair of amorous party-goers couldn't wait until they got home, she didn't want to see it. "I— This is his room and somebody said he was in here. Obviously, he isn't. I'm sorry." She reached behind her for the doorknob. "I didn't mean to disturb you."

"No problem," the woman said. "Zeke's right here. Hold on a sec and I'll see if I can wake him up. He was pretty blasted."

Ariel stood, stock-still, unbelieving, unable to move. That couldn't be Zeke in the bed with that woman. It couldn't be.

"Hey, Zeke. Come on, babe, wake up. You got company."

Ariel heard a grunt and then a muffled curse. A man's voice, certainly, but surely not Zeke's. Surely not. And then the gray lump in the bed separated into two distinct shapes and the bedside light came on.

"What the hell's going on?" Zeke demanded irritably. "Who the hell are—" And then he caught sight of Ariel, standing frozen by the door. "Jesus, *Ariel!*"

They stared at each other for a second or two, both of them speechless with shock. And then Zeke uttered a vicious oath and scrambled out of the bed, uncovering the woman beside him in his haste.

She was naked.

And he was naked.

Ariel lifted one hand to her mouth, as if to hold back a cry, and groped behind her for the doorknob.

"This isn't what it looks like," Zeke said, grabbing for his pants as the woman in his bed pulled the covers back up over her. "Just let me get my jeans on and—"

With a muffled sob, Ariel turned away and yanked open the bedroom door.

"Dammit, Ariel, wait a minute. Don't go. I—"

But she was already gone, flying through the apartment out the front door. By the time Zeke got his jeans on and halfway zipped up, she was already racing down the hall to the courtyard entrance. He was just in time to catch the door before it swung closed. She swerved sharply, veering away from the drunk lying on his back in the shadow of an overhanging balcony, and then stumbled against the chaise longue, almost falling over the entwined occupants before she righted herself and ran on.

"Dammit, Ariel. Wait. Please. I can explain, I—" Zeke hit something with his foot and went down, sprawling over the drunk Ariel had managed to avoid.

He caught himself on his palms, pushing himself up to his knees, and then realized that he'd put his hands in something wet and sticky, and that the same something was seeping through the knees of his jeans. He lifted his palms, turning them toward the moonlight. It was blood.

1

ZEKE BLACKSTONE followed the slender, miniskirted receptionist down the wide, plushly carpeted hallway with all the reluctance of a truant schoolboy on his way to the principal's office.

He barely noticed the tastefully extravagant bouquets of fresh flowers that bloomed atop slender marble columns placed at intervals along the hallway. Or the faint scent of orange blossoms and money that perfumed the air. Or the muted, lilting sounds of the romantic Bach concerto being piped in through hidden speakers. Or that many of the famous faces in the soft-focus wedding photographs hanging on the pale cream, silk-covered walls were of people he knew and worked with. He didn't even notice the deliberately swaying hips of the receptionist.

His gaze was riveted on the ornately carved door at the end of the hall, his entire attention focused on what—*who*—was waiting for him on the other side. The expression in his dark eyes was identical to one a man might wear as he approached the judge's bench for sentencing—after having already been tried and found guilty of all the charges against him.

"You're the last one to arrive, Mr. Blackstone," the receptionist said, making sure she gave him her best side as she turned her head to smile over her shoulder. "But I doubt you've missed much."

"Missed much?" Zeke muttered, his eyes still on the door.

"Of the planning. Mr. Wescott and Ms. Fine always start the first meeting off with coffee and a little casual chitchat. To put everyone at ease, you know." She flashed him another twinkling smile, in case he'd missed the first one. "Here we are," she said brightly, reaching out to put her hand on the ornate gilt door handle.

Zeke reached out and grasped her forearm, halting her in midmotion. "Who's everyone?" he asked, stalling for time. He knew very well who "everyone" was. That was the problem.

The receptionist frowned prettily, managing to look puzzled without a single line creasing her smooth forehead. "Excuse me?"

Zeke nodded at the door. "In there. Who's everyone?"

"Oh." The frown disappeared, replaced by a look of eager helpfulness. "The bride and groom. The bride's mother. The maid of honor. And Mr. Wescott and Ms. Fine, of course." She smiled again, full face this time and giving it all she had. "Mr. Wescott asked me to show you in the minute you arrived."

"I'll show myself in," Zeke said, and let go of her arm to reach for the door handle himself. "Thanks," he added, giving her an absent nod of dismissal. "You've been very helpful."

Miffed at being so thoroughly ignored by such an infamous and internationally acclaimed lady's man, the receptionist turned on her heel and sashayed back down the hall to her desk. It was a stellar performance but a wasted one. Her audience of one was hardly paying attention.

Zeke stood in front of the door, his hand on the knob, paralyzed with what he could only describe to himself as an acute case of stage fright. Which was ridiculous, because he'd never suffered from stage fright in his life. He took a deep, steadying breath and reached up to loosen his too tight tie, only to realize that, as usual, he wasn't wearing one. He ran his hand through his hair instead, brushing the unruly waves back off his forehead, then took another deep breath, told himself to quit acting like an idiot, and pushed open the door. It got away from him, banging back against the gilt doorstop from the unintentional force of his inward thrust.

Conversation stopped abruptly at his noisy, unceremonious entrance. Six heads turned toward him. Six pairs of eyes widened in recognition and surprise.

"Sorry," Zeke mumbled sheepishly, careful not to look into any one pair of eyes. Or into one pair of eyes in particular.

For a second or two more the six people around the graceful, cabriole-legged conference table—delicate Limoges coffee cups or frosted petits fours halfway to their mouths—remained frozen in place, Zeke stood stock-still in the doorway, like an actor who'd forgotten his lines. The air crackled with a strange tension, ripe with anticipation, and everyone seemed to be holding his or her breath. And then a young woman put her coffee cup down and jumped up from her seat, breaking the strained silence.

"Oh, Dad. Dad, you're here! Finally." Cameron Blackstone flew across the room with her characteristic enthusiasm and threw herself into her father's arms, confident that she would be caught. "I was afraid you'd

chickened out at the last minute and weren't coming,"
she said and hugged him. Hard.

Zeke Blackstone hugged her back, holding her close
and pressing a kiss on the top of her head. "My plane
was late. And the traffic was a mess." He lifted one
broad Armani clad shoulder in an apologetic shrug. "I
always forget how impossible L.A. traffic is, even when
there's no earthquake damage to contend with," he
said, gazing down into eyes nearly as dark as his own.
He ran his hand lightly over her hair, noting, as always, that it was the same pale golden blond as her
mother's. "I'm really sorry, honey. I hope it didn't cause
any problems."

"No harm done," Cameron said, instantly forgiving
him. "You're here now. That's all that matters." She
tucked her arm into the crook of his, turning him toward the conference table. "Come and meet Michael,"
she said, her voice warm with love and pride as she
drew her father across the room to meet her fiancé.

The young man in question was already on his feet.
"It's a pleasure to finally meet you, sir," he said and offered his hand. "Cami talks about you all the time." He
flashed an easy grin, showing a glimpse of white, even
teeth. "According to her, you practically hung the
moon."

"Really?" Zeke cast a teasing sideways look at his
daughter as he took the young man's hand. *Cami?* His
daughter hadn't allowed anyone to call her by her
childhood nickname since...well, since she was a child.
"All I've heard for the last two months is how wonderful you are. Every time I've talked to her lately, it's been
'Michael this' and 'Michael that.' I've been expecting to
meet a cross between Mel Gibson, Albert Einstein and
the archangel Gabriel."

"Oh, Dad," Cameron said, blushing slightly as she swatted her father on the arm. "I never said anything like that."

But Zeke ignored his daughter for the moment, his eyes narrowing slightly as he studied the young man who intended to marry his precious only child. He decided he liked what he saw. Michael Everett had calm, intelligent blue eyes, a confident, easygoing manner and a firm handshake. But how did a father *really* know if a suitor was good enough to be entrusted with his daughter's happiness and well-being?

"If you ever hurt her," Zeke said, very softly, "I'll come after you with a loaded gun and a skinning knife. And you'll be begging me to use the first before I've finished with the second."

"Dad! For heaven's sake," Cameron protested. "What an awful thing to say. Michael doesn't know what a big tease you are," she chided gently. "He might take you seriously."

Zeke didn't shift his gaze from that of his prospective son-in-law. "Michael had better take me seriously."

"I do, sir. Very seriously." Michael's Adam's apple bobbed as he swallowed but his gaze remained steady. "And you don't have to worry, sir. I promise I'll take care of her," he vowed. "Always."

Zeke nodded, satisfied. "See that you do," he said, and released the young man's hand.

"Oh, for heaven's sake." Cameron rolled her eyes. "Anyone would think I was some poor defenseless half-wit about to be handed over to Bluebeard or something."

"Your father just wants to be sure I'll take proper care of you," Michael said.

"Completely ignoring the fact that I can take care of myself," Cameron retorted, her tone hovering somewhere between amusement and feminine indignation. "And have been for a while now."

"Now, honey," Zeke drawled, his tone deliberately—and provocatively—placating. "Don't go getting all upset. Neither one of us meant to imply that you couldn't take care of yourself." He cocked an eyebrow at his future son-in-law. "Did we, Michael?" he prompted.

"No, sir," Michael agreed, instantly following his soon-to-be father-in-law's lead. "That wasn't the implication at all. I would never suggest that Cami couldn't take care of herself." He sighed, the epitome of the long-suffering, put-upon male. "I know better than to do anything like that."

Zeke smiled his approval at Michael's quick uptake, flashing the lazy good-natured grin that made men think they might like to share a beer with him—and women think of sharing something more intimate. "See there?" he said to his daughter. "Michael didn't mean to insult your feminist principles." His dark eyes twinkled wickedly. "And neither did—"

"You remember Susan, don't you, Dad?" Cameron said pointedly, discreetly tugging on her father's arm to move him along. "She's going to be my maid of honor, so I wanted her to be in on the planning right from the first." Cameron flashed a quick smile at her best friend. "I promised her I wouldn't even consider a bridesmaid dress she didn't absolutely love, too."

"Yes, of course, I remember Susan. Vividly," Zeke said, disengaging his arm from his daughter's as he leaned down to kiss the young woman's cheek. "Playing chaperon while the two of you ran amok up and down the Côte d'Azur last summer is the reason for all these gray hairs." He ran a hand through the silver-flecked hair at his temple. "It put *'Til Death Do Us Part* seriously over budget, too, if I remember rightly."

"That was three summers ago, Dad," Cameron corrected him.

"Three? Are you sure?"

"Between my junior and senior year at UCLA," she assured him. "And *'Til Death Do Us Part* went over budget because your leading man had a problem with the bottle. He ended up at the Betty Ford Clinic after the movie wrapped, if *I* remember rightly," she said, giving him the same innocent look he'd bestowed on her just a minute ago. "And you had those gray hairs way before then, too."

Zeke winced in mock pain. "The child doesn't understand the concept of dramatic license," he said dolefully. "And she has no respect for her old man. I hope you're more respectful to your father, Susan."

Susan didn't even try to hide her smile. "I do my best," she said.

"Good. That's good," Zeke said, absently patting his daughter's hand when she slipped it back into the crook of his elbow. "Maybe you could give Cam—"

He turned his head sharply, reacting to the tug on his arm, and met his daughter's gaze. There was a split second of heat from both of them—her at him for dragging his feet, him at her for forcing him to face something he'd rather not. Their gazes cooled almost instantly, softening into understanding and appeal on her part, melting into grudging acceptance and resignation on his. Stalling wouldn't change a thing, and he knew it. His only child had asked this one simple thing of him and he was going to give it to her. Even if it killed him.

"Dad, this is Alan Wescott, one of our wedding consultants."

"It's a pleasure to meet you, Mr. Blackstone," Alan Wescott said as they shook hands. "A real pleasure."

"My pleasure, as well," Zeke said graciously.

"And his partner, Leslie Fine."

"Ms. Fine," Zeke said, unconsciously adding an appreciative twinkle to his gracious smile.

"Leslie, please," the woman said. "We're all going to get to know each pretty well before the wedding day arrives."

"Leslie," Zeke said with a polite nod.

And then there was only one person left in the room he hadn't greeted. His gut tightened. His heartbeat quickened. His nerves began to scrape against the inside of his skin, in a way they hadn't done since his earliest days in Hollywood. He did what he had done back then, taking a brief second to center himself. *You can do this, Blackstone*, he told himself. *You can do anything you put your mind to. It isn't really going to kill you.* And then he turned, and faced the mother of his only child.

She was still heartbreakingly beautiful but, then, he had known she would be. Like everyone else who owned a television set, he'd watched her career progress from the beautiful daughter on *Family Fortune*, to the beautiful young career woman in *On My Own*, to the beautiful wife on *Maggie and Me*. For the past two years, her beautiful face had been plastered all over the advertising landscape as Gavino Cosmetics' symbol of Ageless Beauty.

And ageless she was.

Her eyes hadn't lost any of their sparkle over the years; they were the same vividly intense shade of blue they had been when she was eighteen. Her hair, though no longer cascading down her back like Alice in Wonderland, was still the same pale, gleaming golden blond. Her lips, even under a coating of precisely applied peach lipstick, were still deliciously kissable. But it was the planes and angles of her small, fine-boned face that made her truly ageless. Truly beautiful. Her always exquisite bone structure had been refined and sharpened by the passing years, adding elegance to what had once been a kind of fragile coltishness.

Standing there, staring at her, Zeke could vividly remember running his fingertips over the delicate bones in her face, tracing the lush shape of her lips and the arch of her brows, telling her how beautiful she was. And she had looked back at him with wonder in those incredible blue eyes of hers.

There was no wonder in them now. Far from it. Her expression was guarded and wary. Suspicious, even, as if she expected him to do or say something that would cause a scene or start a scandal.

He was almost tempted to live down to her expectations. It was what he would have done before, when he was a neophyte actor with a James Dean attitude. It was what he might still do, if she kept looking at him like that. Except for Cameron, he reminded himself. He was doing this for Cameron and it had to be perfect for his adored daughter. With that thought foremost in his mind, he fought down the urge to haul his ex-wife up against him by the lapels of her stylish Carolina Herrera jacket and shake her—or kiss her—senseless.

"Hello, Ariel," he said pleasantly and offered his hand. "Long time, no see."

As opening lines went, it was pretty lame but he'd made the first move and now the ball was in her court.

"Hello, Zeke," she said, and put her hand into his.

It was a mistake.

She knew it the minute their palms touched.

The heat was still there, as strong, as vital, as tempting as it had been the first time he'd ever touched her. It sizzled up her arm like wildfire, heading straight to the hidden core of her. Thank God, there was no chance she would succumb to its lure this time, she thought, belatedly steeling her nerve endings against him. This time she would be strong. Invulnerable. Invincible. *Immune*. Because this time she wasn't a breathless, wide-eyed ingenue, eager to taste life and oh-so-ripe for the plucking. This time, she knew that heat and sizzle was all there was to Zeke Blackstone.

All right, not *all*, she amended grudgingly. In the years since they'd last seen each other, he'd matured into a brilliant actor and then into an even more brilliant director. And he was a good and loving father to their daughter. But he'd been a lousy husband. And not just to her. There had been another ex-wife between then and now, as well as a live-in lover or two ... or three. If one could believe even half of what was printed in the tabloids, he'd also indulged himself in an uncounted number of brief flings, one-night stands and sizzling location romances over the years as well.

Zeke's legendary bad boy charm and sizzling sexuality attracted women like moths to the proverbial flame but it burned them up and burned them out in short order. And she should know. She had the scars to prove it. Not that anyone had ever been—or would ever be—allowed to see those scars. Least of all, the man who had inflicted the wounds that caused them.

She forced her lips into an empty little smile. "It's good to see you, Zeke," she said, feigning a credible and convincing coolness as she withdrew her hand from his.

Without conscious thought, Zeke tightened his fingers on hers, holding her captive for a scant moment longer, silently demanding that she look at him—really look at him, dammit!—before he would let her go. He tried to tell himself it was just a test of wills, a power play, a game of one-upmanship. And, on one level, it was.

It was also a need.

An urgent, burning, utterly inexplicable need.

Loath to let him gain the upper hand, Ariel reluctantly lifted her gaze to his. Wide blue eyes met smoldering brown for the first time in years.

They both felt the pull.

It was primal.

Visceral.

Frighteningly real.

"Is it really good to see me?" Zeke murmured, his voice low and disturbingly intimate. It shivered along her nerve endings, as real and tactile as a touch.

"Yes," Ariel said, aghast to realize she meant it. *Oh, God, I don't want to mean it!* "Yes, of course it is," she added, managing to make the words sound offhand and casual, like a polite social lie one didn't really care if the hearer believed or not.

"It's good to see you again, too, Ariel," he said softly, surprised at just how much he meant it. And how much he wanted her to mean it, too.

And then he let go of her hand and turned to smile down at his anxiously hovering daughter. "What do you say we get this show on the road?" he said jovially, as if he hadn't just been shaken to his very soul. "I had my secretary make reservations for us at Le Dôme at one-thirty."

"Then we'd definitely better get started," Alan Wescott said, inviting everyone to sit down with a wave of his hand. "We've got a lot to cover in this first meeting."

"Where do we start?" Cameron asked, her eyes bright with eagerness.

"We usually find it's best to decide on the type of wedding you want first," Leslie Fine told her. "Formal or casual. Traditional or something more unconventional. We've found that everything else flows from that."

"Definitely a traditional church wedding," Cameron said decisively. "We've already talked to the minister and booked the church for the last Saturday in September."

The two wedding consultants exchanged a startled glance. "Not *this* September, surely?" Wescott asked.

"Yes, this September. I know it's kind of short notice but once we decided to get married, well . . ." Cameron turned her head and smiled at her fiancé. "There just didn't seem to be any point in waiting. And the end of September was the soonest we could get the church."

"But that leaves us with less than six weeks to plan an entire wedding," Wescott pointed out.

"That isn't going to be a problem, is it?" Zeke asked, subtly letting the two consultants know that it had better not be, not if they wanted their company to orchestrate the Blackstone-Everett wedding—and collect the fat check that would go with it.

"No. No, problem," Leslie Fine rushed to assure him. "We'll have to adjust the usual timetable a bit but I'm certain we can accommodate your wishes." She flipped open a three-ring binder covered in smooth cream-colored leather and already stamped with the names of the happy couple. "Have you decided on a time of day, as well?"

"Well, we thought maybe ten o'clock for the actual ceremony?" Cameron suggested. "And then the reception at home afterward," she added, referring to the Beverly Hills mansion where she'd grown up, and not the Brentwood condo she'd been renting for the past two years. She glanced across the table for confirmation. "Mom? Is that okay with you?"

"Of course, darling. Whatever you want." Ariel smiled at her daughter, trying not to let her memories of another wedding spoil her joy in this one. It didn't help that the man who'd stood beside her then was sitting beside her now, bringing it all back in every painful detail. "It's your wedding, Cameron, and your decision. I want you to have exactly what you want."

She'd made no decisions, voiced no opinions concerning her own wedding to Cameron's father, not about the place or the time, not the guest list or the food or the bridesmaids. She hadn't even seen her wedding dress until it was time to put it on.

"Then ten o'clock," Cameron said. "With a sit-down champagne brunch and dancing on the patio after. How does that sound, Mom?"

"Perfectly lovely."

"Dad?"

"Sounds like a good plan to me," Zeke said decisively, as if his whole attention were riveted on the discussion of his daughter's upcoming wedding. A part of him was. His daughter's wedding day was, after all, one of the most important days in her life and, thus, in his.

But another part of him was in utter shock, reeling from discovery that he was still apparently ass-end-over-teakettle in love with a woman he hadn't seen since their own wedding day, nearly twenty-five years ago.

2

"OH, COME ON, MOM. It'll be fun," Cameron coaxed. "Le Dôme is one of your favorite restaurants. We can talk about the wedding some more."

"I'd love to, darling—you know that," Ariel said, lying just as graciously as she did everything else. "But I can't today. I have a meeting with the Gavino Cosmetics people this afternoon about renewing my contract for the Ageless Beauty campaign."

"Call them and reschedule it," Zeke suggested.

Ariel ignored him, pretending to herself that he didn't exist. It was a useful skill. One she'd had twenty-five years to perfect. "Why don't you and Susan come over to the house for lunch tomorrow?" she said to her daughter. "I'll have Eleanor make chicken salad sandwiches and iced tea and we can look through the bridal magazines Leslie gave you and try to find a style of bridesmaid's dress you both love." She smiled at her future son-in-law. "Michael can come and look at bridesmaid dresses, too, if he'd like."

"No, thanks." Michael gave a mock shudder. "I think I'll pass on that. Talking about fashion gives me hives."

"Well, if you change your mind, lunch will be served at twelve sharp," she informed him as she turned away to give her daughter a quick hug. "Have a nice lunch, darling. I'll see you tomorrow. You, too, I hope," she said to her daughter's maid of honor. Then, with a gracious smile and a regal little wave, she turned and left—

without having either directly spoken to or acknowl-
edged her ex-husband beyond their first few words of
greeting.

Which was just like her, Zeke thought, feeling a
strange mixture of admiration and irritation. Ariel had
always had the maddening ability to ignore anything
she didn't want to see, just like a queen stepping over
peasants in the street. She'd always had exquisite manners, too, but twenty-five years ago they'd been the
rather grave good manners of an extremely well-
behaved little girl. Now, she used them like a double-
bladed rapier, cutting him cold without drawing a single drop of blood.

"YOU'RE SURE the Malibu house is uninhabitable?" Zeke
said, speaking to his secretary as he exited the Le Dôme
parking lot and turned his rented Jag onto Sunset
Boulevard. "Hell, Patsy, the contractor's had his crew
out there—what? nearly a year now?—and you're telling me it still isn't finished? Just how much damage was
there from the quake?"

"It's not the structural repairs that are taking so long,
it's the bathrooms," Patsy said drily. "Remember all
that imported Italian marble you decided you needed?
Well, apparently, the guys who mine it or quarry it, or
whatever it is one does to marble, are on strike. I've
booked you into a suite at the Regent Beverly Wilshire
but I can find you a house to rent if you think you're
going to be in L.A. for a while this time."

"No, don't bother. Cameron's wedding is only six
weeks away. I guess I can survive at the Regent for that
long."

"It's a tough life," Patsy said drily. "But somebody's
gotta live it."

ZEKE WAS FORCED to make two detours due to construction crews and road repair, ending up farther west on Wilshire than he wanted to be. To get to the Regent Beverly Wilshire hotel, he had to turn around and go back the other way. Grumbling under his breath, he turned right onto a side street, and then right again, into an empty driveway. He glanced into the rearview mirror and pushed in the clutch, ready to shift the Jag into reverse—and then stopped and stared. Something about the three-story apartment building reflected in the rearview mirror looked oddly familiar.

Like so many older buildings in Southern California, this one was primarily Spanish in design, with arched windows and wrought iron railings. The stucco walls were faded, sun-washed pink, the eaves were trimmed in equally faded turquoise blue. There was a turret jutting up on one side of the building, vaguely Moorish in design, and a leafy banana tree in front.

"Well, I'll be damned," Zeke said, finally recognizing the Bachelor Arms apartment building. "It's my past, come back to haunt me."

He'd lived there, once upon a time. He and Ethan Roberts and Eric Shannon and Eric's younger brother... What was his name? Jack, that was it. Jack Shannon. God, they'd had some great times in the old BA. And some terrible ones, too.

He'd made love to Ariel for the very first time one perfect summer afternoon in the small front bedroom of apartment 1-G. And then he'd lost her, less than two months later, in that very same bedroom. Other people had lost things there, too.

Jack Shannon had lost his older brother.

Eric Shannon had lost his life.

And, yet, for all that, it was the good times Zeke remembered most as he sat in the rented Jag, staring at the legendary old building in his rearview mirror. The hopes and dreams they'd all had. The plans they'd made. The sense of limitless possibilities spread out in front of them like a sumptuous banquet. The innocent belief that the whole world was theirs for the taking. It had been a heady time. Exciting and terrifying. Full of passion and promise.

And it was over.

Finis.

Dead as the proverbial doornail.

Zeke sighed, feeling nostalgic and just a little melancholy as he shifted the Jag into reverse. He backed out of the driveway and shifted into first, checking the side mirror for oncoming traffic. A movement in front of the Bachelor Arms caught his eye. A man was standing at the wrought iron gate that stretched across the entrance to the courtyard, trying to slide a rectangular piece of shiny white signboard into the metal frame affixed to the decorative bars.

Zeke could hardly believe his eyes. "Amberson," he said, instantly recognizing the building superintendent despite the nearly twenty-five years that had passed since the last time he'd seen him. The strange little man had hardly changed a bit. He was still small and wiry, and still as bald as an egg.

He stepped back from the gate as Zeke sat there watching, his shining bald head tilted as he surveyed his handiwork. Zeke had no trouble reading the neatly hand-lettered sign from where he was. Apartment for rent, it said. Inquire Manager's Office.

Zeke decided it was an omen.

And, besides, he'd lied to Patsy. He couldn't stand six weeks in a hotel, after all. Not even the Regent Beverly Wilshire.

"CURRENT TENANTS'LL be out by the end of the week," Amberson said when Zeke went in to inquire about the apartment. "I gotta get it cleaned, and the faucet in the bathroom sink needs fixing but the place don't need painting. I can have it ready for you by Monday, if you're interested."

"I'd like to see it first," Zeke said, in a belated effort to be practical. "If it wouldn't inconvenience the current tenants."

"Don't see why it should. Ain't nobody home." Amberson opened his apartment door, then stood aside, pointedly waiting for Zeke to precede him into the hall. It wasn't from politeness, Zeke knew, but sprang from a basic distrust of people. Amberson simply didn't want anyone to be alone in his apartment-cum-office, even for a split second.

Zeke obliged him by exiting the apartment, and then, hands stuffed into the pockets of his elegant gunmetal gray Armani slacks, stood aside, waiting as the wiry little man carefully triple-locked his apartment door.

"This way," Amberson said, and headed off down the hallway without a backward glance, as if he didn't particularly care whether his prospective tenant was following him or not.

Zeke gave a mental shrug, more amused than anything else at being treated like a nobody. It wasn't personal, he knew; the Amberson he remembered had treated everyone as if they were nobody.

They made their way out a side door that opened onto the courtyard of the apartment building, obviously heading for the corresponding door which opened into the hallway on the other side of the pebbled concrete patio.

It was exactly the way Zeke remembered it. The luxuriantly overgrown hibiscus and trailing bougainvillea, the faint outline in the concrete patio where the pool had been filled in, the cool shadows cast by the overhanging balconies from the second and third floor apartments. He shivered a bit, feeling a cold finger trace its way up his spine as he stepped over the exact spot where he'd stumbled over Eric Shannon's lifeless body all those years ago.

What an awful night that had been! The screams. The sirens. The blood. He'd never seen so much blood in his life—before or since. He'd been forced to endure the feel of it on his body for what had seemed like hours while the police took their photographs and asked their questions. And the smell; he'd never forget the dead, coppery smell of Eric's blood.

"You want to see that apartment or not?" Amberson demanded, breaking into Zeke's morbid reverie.

Zeke refocused his eyes on the present and saw the superintendent standing with one hand on the open door, a scowl of impatience on his face. *If I had any sense,* Zeke thought suddenly, *I'd say no and get the hell out of here.* It was no good, digging up the past. "Yes, I want to see the apartment," he said.

Amberson grunted and let go of the door.

Zeke caught it before it swung closed and hurried to follow Amberson down the second narrow hallway. He almost bumped into the superintendent when he stopped, abruptly and unexpectedly, in front of apartment 1-G.

"I don't believe it," Zeke murmured under his breath.

"Changed your mind?" Amberson asked, almost as if he'd been expecting that reaction. Waiting for it, in fact.

Zeke gave him a searching look but could see no sign of recognition in the other man's pale gray eyes. "No. I haven't changed my mind." *At least, not yet.* "Let's see it."

Amberson yanked at the chain running from his belt loop to the pocket of his baggy chinos, pulling a jangling ring of keys out of the deep front pocket. With no fumbling, he found the proper key and inserted it into the lock.

The door to Zeke's past opened on well-oiled hinges.

Amberson stepped back and waved him in. "After you," he invited with the first show of real civility Zeke had ever seen him display.

Brushing by him with barely a glance, Zeke stepped over the threshold and walked back into his past. Nothing happened. No deafening thunderclaps, no flashes of lightning warning him not to proceed further. There was no particular feeling of dread or elation, either. It was just an apartment, a place he had once lived in. Breathing a small sigh of relief and, yet, feeling strangely, vaguely disappointed—didn't what had happened here deserve some sort of divine recognition?—Zeke started down the narrow hallway to the living room.

The apartment was nicer than he'd remembered, even with the neatly stacked piles of boxes and the packing materials scattered on the floor. It was light and airy, with an elegant old world charm he'd been too young and stupid to appreciate the first time around. Of course, he thought, it probably hadn't helped that the decorating style of the time had dictated psychedelic colors, beanbag chairs, cheap beaded curtains and black light posters on the walls.

The walls were painted a soft, creamy white, now. The high, arched windows overlooking the courtyard were flanked by slatted wooden shutters. The floors were hardwood, polished to a glossy sheen. Zeke moved through the rooms of the apartment slowly, his hands stuffed deep in his pants pockets, taking it all in, observing, remembering. A wide graceful archway opened off the living room onto the dining room, with a small efficiency kitchen beyond that which, in turn, led back into the living room. He walked down a short hall to the two small bedrooms and a surprisingly large bathroom with an old-fashioned claw-footed tub and pale aqua tile running halfway up the walls. It was all eerily the same, he thought, right down to the massive old mirror on the living room wall.

It was a ridiculous piece of expensive Victorian frippery, at least four feet wide by five feet tall, framed in pewter that had been elaborately cast with dozens of roses and ribbonlike scrolls. There had been some legend connected with the mirror, Zeke recalled. Some curse. He couldn't quite remember what it entailed, except that it had had something to do with a young starlet who was rumored to have drowned in the pool that had once graced the courtyard. He'd always thought that particular story had been dreamed up by someone who'd taken one too many drug-induced trips.

"Did you ever see her?" Amberson asked.

Zeke shifted his gaze from the mirror to the building super. "Did I ever see who?"

"The woman in the mirror." Amberson lifted his chin at the mirror. "Some say it's the ghost of Jeannie Masters, the girl who drowned in the pool that used to be down there in the courtyard. That's why it was filled in, you know. Nobody knows whether it was an accident, or if she drowned herself on purpose, or if somebody held her under 'til she stopped breathing. She's supposed to live in that mirror there, and she only shows herself when somebody's life is about to change somehow."

"Really?" Zeke murmured, trying not to encourage the superintendent. He wasn't the least bit interested in ghost stories.

"Sometimes the change is for the better and the person who sees her gets their dream. But mostly it's a change for the worse," Amberson said with relish. "There was a girl, saw her the night of the party you guys had. Your old roommate saw her, too. That one who's running for Congress now? He saw her the day before he got the part in that soap opera he was in. The one that started his career." Amberson's gray eyes glittered. "Told me all about it one night."

"Ethan Roberts? He saw the—" And then Zeke realized the significance of Amberson's remarks. "You know who I am," he said, and he wasn't referring to the fame he'd achieved via the silver screen.

Amberson nodded. "You're the kid who fell over Shannon's body that night."

"Well, why the hell didn't you say something when I first came in and asked about the apartment, if you knew who I was?"

"What for? It wouldn't make no difference to anything, would it?" Amberson shrugged. "Couldn't see no point in bringing it up, not if you wasn't going to take the place."

"Point?" Zeke said, inexplicably irritated. "No, I guess there was no point, but it certainly would have been the polite thing to—"

"Hello?" A lilting female voice, accented with the soft vowels of the deep South, came floating from the direction of the open front door to the apartment. "Mr. Amberson, is that you?"

"Dammit, Angel—" the speaker was male, his voice rich with exasperated affection "—don't go running in there like that. For all you know, an ax murderer could have broken in while we were gone."

"An ax murderer would have used his ax to break the door down," the woman said. "I didn't see any signs of dam— Oh, all right. You go first, if it'll make you happy."

A man appeared from down the front hallway with a brown paper grocery sack cradled in one arm. He was as lean and rangy as a big cat, with a cat's watchful eyes and instinctive wariness. He tensed when he saw Zeke standing in his living room, automatically shifting his stance to keep the woman safely out of reach behind him. And then he caught sight of the superintendent and relaxed. Infinitesimally.

"Amberson," he said, a question in his voice and eyes.

"I got a prospective tenant here," Amberson said, jerking his head toward Zeke. "Showing him the place."

"See?" the woman said, giving the man a saucy little smile as she slipped past him. "I told you it wasn't an ax murderer."

Zeke smiled his most charming, aw-shucks, I'm-really-perfectly-harmless smile. "I'm sorry if we startled you."

"Oh, you didn't startle me," she said, returning his smile with one of her own. "My husband's the one with the suspicious mind." She held out her hand. "I'm Faith Shannon. And this is my husband—"

"Jack," Zeke said, unconsciously interrupting her. "My God, *you're Jack Shannon.*"

"Yes, that's right."

Suddenly uneasy, Faith shifted her gaze back and forth between the two men. They were staring at each other as if they'd just seen a ghost. "Jack?" she said hesitantly, reaching out to put her hand on her husband's arm.

"It's all right, Angel. This is an old—" he hesitated briefly, as if he weren't quite sure of the proper word "—friend of mine. I haven't seen him for twenty-five years. Not since right after Eric died." He shifted the grocery sack he held so he could offer his right hand. "How are you, Zeke?"

"Stunned," Zeke said as they shook hands. "Completely stunned. I had no idea you were the tenant Amberson was talking about. Or that the apartment I was going to look at was 1-G. He never said a—" Zeke broke off in midsentence and turned to face the man in question. "Why the hell didn't you say anything about this?" he demanded.

"No point until you decided to take it," Amberson said, unperturbed by Zeke's hostility. "So, have you?"

"Have I what?"

"Decided to take it."

Zeke didn't even have to think about. "Yes," he said. "I'll take it."

Amberson nodded, as if he'd known the answer all along. "Stop by my office before you leave," he said, and headed for the front door. "I'll have the rental agreement ready for you to sign." He paused, waiting until he had everyone's attention. "Ask the Shannons about the woman in the mirror," he said, his voice low and dramatic. "They'll tell you she's real."

Nobody said another word until he had walked down the hall and out the door, closing it firmly behind him.

And then Faith Shannon sighed and shook her head. "Mr. Amberson is a very strange man," she said. "It's very disconcerting."

"It's irritating as hell, is what it is," her husband grumbled.

"But he's right, you know," Faith said to Zeke. She reached out to take the sack of groceries from her husband, transferring it to her hip as she spoke. "The woman in the mirror is real. I've seen her. And so has Jack."

Zeke tried not to look too skeptical. "And did your lives change?"

"Completely," she said blissfully, and smiled at her husband over the top of the grocery sack.

He smiled back and reached out, tenderly brushing back a tendril of hair that lay against her temple.

Zeke felt as if he were watching them kiss. Passionately. He cleared his throat. "Well, I guess I'd better be going. Let you two, um . . . finish your packing."

"Oh, we're finished for the day," Faith said, shifting her attention back to her guest. "I was just going to put on a fresh pot of coffee to go with the baklava—" she tapped the side of the grocery sack "—Jack couldn't resist. You're more than welcome to join us, ah . . ." Her smile was both charming and apologetic. "I'm sorry. I guess I didn't catch your name."

Jack Shannon gave a muffled snort of laughter at the quick look of surprise that crossed Zeke's face; being so completely unrecognized was a novel experience for him. "Angel, this is Zeke Blackstone," Jack said, before Zeke could introduce himself. "One of Hollywood's brightest lights?" he prompted. "Actor. Director. Producer."

"Actor?" she said hesitantly.

"You know, like in the movies?" he teased gently, then flashed a grin at Zeke. "You'll have to forgive her. She's only seen about five movies in her entire life."

"It's been more than fi— Oh, my goodness." Faith put her free hand to her chest, her eyes wide as she stared at their guest. "Of course. Zeke Blackstone. I read an article about you in *People* magazine while I was waiting at the dentist's office last week. It was about your new movie . . . ah . . ."

"*Sacred Ground,*" Zeke supplied.

"Yes, that was it. *Sacred Ground.* It looked like a very interesting movie," she said earnestly. "The article predicted it would be a big hit."

"Let's hope so," Zeke agreed drily.

Faith shook her head. "I can't believe I didn't recognize you."

"It happens all the time," Zeke lied.

But Faith wasn't quite as innocent as she looked. "I doubt it," she said with a sweet smile, "but thank you for trying to make me feel better." She hefted the bag of groceries, resettling it on her hip. "I'll have that coffee ready in a few minutes."

"And I should be going," Zeke said. "I've intruded long enough."

"Nonsense. You haven't intruded at all," Faith said firmly. "I know you and Jack must have a lot to talk about." She looked up at her husband. "So, please, sit down, both of you, while I go make the coffee."

There was a second or two of silence after she left the room. "Only five movies in her entire life?" Zeke said, his tone somewhere between scandalized and incredulous.

Jack grinned. "Hard to believe, isn't it?" He motioned Zeke to take a seat on a long brown leather sofa. "But that's Faith. She had a rather sheltered upbringing."

"She's a lovely woman. You're very lucky."

"Yes, I am." Jack said simply. He gave Zeke a level look. "So . . . are you really moving in here?"

"Just temporarily," Zeke said quickly, suddenly feeling as if he had to justify himself to Eric Shannon's brother for staying in the apartment building where Eric had died. "Until my daughter's wedding is over or the construction on my house is finished, whichever comes first."

Jack nodded understandingly. "I was drawn back, too," he said. "Temporarily. And it changed my life." He glanced at the big ornate mirror on the wall. "Maybe it's your turn now."

3

SHE DREAMED ABOUT HIM that night. Vivid dreams. Heated dreams. Dreams that left her damp and aching and feeling oh, so desperately alone. She awoke in the early morning hours, flushed and fevered, with her fragile white silk nightgown twisted around her thighs and her pillow clutched to her breasts. There were tears on her cheeks.

It had been years since she'd dreamed about him. Years longer since she'd cried over his memory. So many years that she'd thought . . . hoped . . . prayed she was finally, completely over him for good. And then, with just one look, one touch, one whispered exchange in a room full of people, and she was on that emotional roller coaster ride all over again.

Aching for him again.

Crying for him again.

With a strangled moan of denial and rage, Ariel threw back the white satin Porthault sheet that covered her. If she couldn't sleep without dreaming about him, then she wouldn't sleep at all.

She'd done it before. And survived.

She'd survive it again.

She slid across the big empty bed and got up, automatically reaching for the silk robe that lay across the tufted white velvet fainting couch at the foot, automatically stepping into the quilted white satin mules that sat, side by side, beneath it. But it was too warm to put the robe on, her skin was too hot and . . . itchy. The mules were too confining. Tossing the robe across the foot of the bed, kicking off the mules, she walked barefoot across the plush carpet to the tall glass doors leading out onto the terrace.

She wanted to fling open the doors and feel the cool air on her skin but the alarm would go off if she did that, bringing the Beverly Hills police and the people from the private security company. She pressed her palms against the cool glass, instead, and then her cheek and her breasts and her thighs, willing it to draw the heat from her body, knowing it couldn't.

She pulled away from the glass door with an anguished cry and hurried across the bedroom, her bare feet sinking into the thick white carpet, her thin silk nightgown floating out behind her. She jerked open her bedroom door, leaving it gaping behind her, and ran down the wide, curving staircase, a ghostly apparition flying through the dark, shadowed house as if she were being pursued by demons. She paused at the back door for a moment and took a deep breath, calming herself long enough to remember the security code and punch it in. And then she was flying again, running lightly across the smooth gray quarry tiles to the very edge of the pool.

She hovered there for a long moment, her arms at her sides, her bare toes curled over the tiled edge of the pool, watching the moonlight glimmer on the surface of the water. It was almost enough. And then a breeze rose up out of nowhere, playfully lifting her hair from her shoulders, pressing her thin silk nightgown against her body, caressing her skin like a lover's teasing fingers. And it was suddenly all too much to bear.

Without thinking about appearances or the inappropriateness of it, without thinking of anything except finding relief from the heat that plagued her, Ariel lifted her hands, each to the opposite shoulder, and pushed the straps of her nightgown off. It fluttered down her slender body, soft as a sigh, and pooled around her feet. She stepped out of it, a beautiful butterfly leaving her silken chrysalis behind, and dove into the water.

The first shocking chill of it was just what she needed, sending a jolt through her overheated senses, soothing the itch that seemed to come from inside her skin. She gave herself up to it, letting the momentum of her dive send her gliding along the bottom of the pool. She surfaced at the shallow end, pressing her hands against the wide, tiled steps for leverage, pushing up and out of the water, her head back, her spine arched so that her thick, shoulder-length hair was slicked away from her face as she broke the surface.

The breeze was there to meet her. It played over her wet skin, first cooling, then caressing it, causing goose flesh to ripple across her arms and her nipples to pull tight and pucker as if they'd been touched. She pressed her hands to her breasts and sank back down into the water. It danced around her like a lover bent on seduction, lapping at her shoulders, undulating against her stomach, swirling between her thighs.

With an inarticulate sound, part a cry of dismay, part a sigh of surrender, Ariel rolled over onto her back and let the water cradle her . . . let the memories take her.

They were all there, hovering at the edge of her mind, as crystal clear, as real, as immediate, as if they had happened the week or the day or the hour before, instead of twenty-five years ago.

The first time he had touched her.
The first time he had kissed her.
The first time he had made her cry.

"I DON'T CARE how brilliant he's supposed to be," Constance Cameron fumed. "He's crude and arrogant, and he's stepping all over your lines. And, what's more," she said accusingly, her red-lacquered finger pointed directly at her daughter, "you're letting him get away with it."

"Mother, please," Ariel pleaded, "it was just a read through. And he's supposed to be crude and arrogant. He's in character."

"In character, my eye," Constance snapped. "That young man is uncivilized and oversexed by nature. And I don't care where the studio found him or what they say about this so-called great talent of his, he's all wrong for this part. Worse, he's all wrong for *you*. You have an image to protect."

"Mother, please. Someone might hear you," Ariel said, nervously eyeing the young man in question.

He lounged negligently atop the chopped Harley hog where they were supposed to be playing their first scene. One foot was propped up on the gas tank, one elbow braced behind him on the leather seat as he flirted indolently with the script girl. Already in costume, he wore heavy black motorcycle boots, tight faded jeans with a peace sign sewn on one knee and a ribbed white tank style undershirt that fit his leanly muscled torso like the skin on a grape and showed off his deep tan to perfection. His hair was dark and thick, tumbling over his ears and the back of his neck, falling nearly to his shoulders. He wore a red bandanna tied around his forehead to keep it out of his face.

Ensconced there atop the huge black motorcycle, like a young prince on his throne, he was the quintessential bad boy of every good girl's secret dreams—wild and disreputable and as cocky as a prizewinning rooster. It made Ariel go all weak in the knees just to look at him.

Not that she'd ever admit it out loud, not in a million years. Especially not within earshot of her mother.

"I don't care if he hears me," Constance said, knowing very well who her daughter meant by "someone." "I don't care if everyone on the set hears me. This is your career we're talking about, Ariel. I never should have let you talk me into allowing you to do this movie. You were doing just fine playing Chrissy."

"I've been playing Chrissy since I was eleven years old." *Too good to be true, perfect, boring, predictable Chrissy Fortune.* "And everybody says the show probably won't last more than another two or three seasons, anyway. You know that. So I couldn't keep playing her forever. And you did agreed I should try something different," Ariel reminded her mother.

"Not this different." Constance shook her head. "What will your fans think when the show starts again next season? Little Chrissy Fortune involved with a ruffian like that?"

"But I'm not playing Chrissy Fortune, mother. This is a completely different character. That's the whole point."

"It's not the—" Constance broke off as the director approached them.

He smiled kindly at Ariel. "Are you ready to try it for the cameras, my dear?"

"Yes, Mr. Ostfield," she said, nervous but willing. "I'm ready."

"No," Constance said imperiously and put her hand on her daughter's arm, stopping her when she would have walked onto the set beside the director. "She is not. Not until you can assure us that that vile young man—" she made the last three words sound like a disease "—isn't going to keep stepping all over Ariel's dialogue. And I want someone to clean up this script. This is not the script I approved. I never agreed to let Ariel allow herself to be pawed. And I want this line in scene twenty-three—" she tapped a manicured nail on the line of dialogue in question "—changed. Ariel Cameron does not use four-letter words."

"No, of course, Ariel does not," Hans Ostfield agreed pleasantly, his Scandinavian accent giving the words a lilting, rhythmic sound. "But Laura Simmons does. And it is Laura Simmons who will say it. And it is not so bad a word, after all."

"Nevertheless, Ariel isn't going to say it."

"Mother, *please*. Can't we discuss this later? That line isn't even in this scene."

"No, we cannot discuss it later. We'll discuss it now. You're not going to use foul language and you're not going to allow yourself to be pawed like some common little tart, and that's final."

Hans Ostfield's expression turned steely. "You are aware, are you not, Mrs. Cameron," he said, still very pleasantly, "that it is entirely within my power to have you removed from this set?"

"You wouldn't dare. I'm Ariel's mother. And Ariel is the star of this production."

Without a word, Hans Ostfield lifted his hand, calling a security guard over with a gesture. "Please escort Mrs. Cameron out," he instructed. "She is not to be allowed on the set while we are filming."

"If I go, Ariel goes," Constance threatened.

"If Ariel goes, she will be in breech of her contract and the studio will put her on suspension. Or, perhaps, sue her. I do not think you want that, do you?"

Constance eyed him for a moment, gauging the strength and determination of her opponent. "We'll just see about this," she said tightly. Turning on her heel, she marched to the door of the sound stage, completely ignoring the security guard who trailed behind her.

Hans turned to his young actress. "I am sorry about that, my dear," he said soothingly. "But I think it will be better this way, don't you? Sometimes a mother is just too close to see that her little girl is growing up."

"Yes, I—" Ariel didn't quite know what to say. No one had ever stood up to her mother like that. She was in awe. "Thank you, Mr. Ostfield."

"Hans, please. We are all friends here. Now—" He took her by the hand. "I know you are nervous. But it is good for you to be nervous in this scene," he assured her, his accent making it necessary for her to listen closely to his every word, "because Laura is nervous, hoping to be kissed for the first time by Judd. It is simple, yes? Take what you feel here—" he touched his loosely curled fist to his chest "—as Ariel and use it to make Laura come to life. Do you understand?"

Ariel nodded. "Yes, Mr. Ostfield...Hans, I understand. I'll try."

"Good. That is all I ask." He patted her hand and then let it go, leaving her to the technicians from Makeup while he had a few words with her male co-star.

"I want you to be gentle when you put your hands on her," he instructed Zeke as he approached him. "You are a rough character, and your words are sometimes rough, yes, but your hands must be gentle when you touch her, to show you are a man with soul. You understand what I am saying? You are already beginning to care for her. A man who cares for a woman treats her gently, especially when she is innocent."

"Got it," Zeke said, nodding as if to himself as he internalized the instructions. "Treat her gently."

"We are going for a take," Hans said, instructing the cast and crew that this wasn't a rehearsal or run-through. "For the freshness of the first kiss, you understand. So even if a mistake is made, I want you to keep going." He paused, waiting while one of the makeup artists rushed in and spritzed Zeke with a spray bottle, leaving a light sheen of fake sweat on his bronzed skin. "Are we ready, then?" Hans demanded.

The two actors nodded.

"Places, everyone," Hans instructed.

Ariel took a deep breath and took her mark in front of the Harley.

"Congratulations, Princess," Zeke said, as he swung his leg over the leather saddle of the bike to sit astride it. "I didn't think you had the guts."

"Guts?"

"I figured America's sweetheart would go running after mommy like a good little girl."

"I'm not—"

"Quiet on the set!"

Ariel obediently closed her mouth, just like the good little girl he'd accused her of being.

"Roll film and . . ." The scene clapper came down. " . . . action."

Zeke slipped seamlessly into his character. "So, Laura," he drawled, "you gonna take that ride with me or not? I know this private little beach over on the west side of the lake where nobody ever goes. It's real nice on a hot day." He smiled wickedly, infusing his words with a wealth of not-so-subtle innuendo. "We could go swimming."

Ariel tried to act the way she thought a girl like Laura Simmons would act when confronted with a boy like Judd. She tried to *be* Laura—spoiled, self-confident and full of herself. She put her fingertip on the handlebar of the Harley and rubbed it slowly up and down the curving slope.

"I don't know if I should," she said, giving him what she hoped was a teasing look from under her lashes. "My father says you're no good. And my mother says you're the dangerous kind. Mad, bad and dangerous to know, is what she said."

Zeke leaned forward, draping his wrists over the handlebars of the bike. "And what do you say, Laura?"

"Oh..." She brought her finger up the curving metal of the handlebars, hesitated for a split second, then trailed it up and over his wrist. Heat zinged up her arm. She licked her lips. "I think you like everyone to *think* you're dangerous but—"

He turned his hand, catching her wrist, and waited until she lifted her gaze to his. "I *am* dangerous," he purred, his eyes glittering hotly as he stared at her. "You keep yanking my chain like you've been doing and you're gonna find out just how dangerous."

It took her a second to remember her next line. "Prove it," she challenged breathlessly.

Without a word, he pulled her around the handlebars by the wrist. When she got close enough, he swung his leg over the saddle of the bike so that he was facing her, then set his hands on either side of her waist and pulled her between his wide-spread thighs. Ariel's hands fluttered for a moment and then settled, gingerly, on his broad bare shoulders.

"You ever been laid on the back of a Harley?" he asked, his voice low and sexy.

"Of course not," she said indignantly.

"You ever been laid at all?"

Ariel shrugged, hoping to convey careless nonchalance with the gesture.

"That mean yes or no?"

"It means it's none of your business," she snapped.

Zeke grinned knowingly. "No, then," he said smugly. "I didn't think so. Hell, you've probably never been kissed, either, have you?"

"I've been kissed plenty," Ariel retorted, forgetting she was quoting words someone else had written for her.

"Yeah, I'll bet," Zeke sneered. "By some sweaty-palmed, pimply-faced high school jock who slobbered all over you like an eager puppy, right?"

"I've been out with college boys, too."

He tsked and shook his head, as if the information disappointed him. "You ever been out with a man, Laura?" he asked and drew her closer to his body, so that the outside of her thighs brushed against the inside of his.

Ariel stiffened her spine and tried not to melt against him until the script called for it.

"A man who'd know how to kiss you without mashing your lips against your teeth?" he murmured and touched his warm lips, oh so lightly, to the corner of her mouth. "A man who'd know just how to touch you—" he ran his hands up her sides, lightly, stopping just short of her breasts "—and where, so you'd beg him to touch you some more? A man who'd treat you like a woman—" his fingers tightened and he pulled her closer, so that her breasts touched his chest "—instead of a spoiled little rich girl?"

It took Ariel a second or two to remember her line. "I'm not a spoiled anything," she said breathlessly.

"Yes, you are." He ran one hand up under the heavy sheaf of her hair to the back of her neck and pulled her even closer. So close that his lips brushed against hers as he spoke. "You're a spoiled, self-centered little bitch," he said, making it sound like the sweetest endearment. And then he opened his mouth over hers.

Ariel forgot all about the script. And the cameras. And the technicians who were watching them. She forgot everything except that she was being kissed within an inch of her life—for the first time in her life—by someone who knew exactly how it was supposed to be done. She sank against him with a soft murmur of approval and acceptance, letting her head fall back under the onslaught of his mouth. She tightened her grip on his bare shoulders, curving her fingers into the sleek, hard muscles beneath them. And when he drew back to speak his next line, she leaned into him and lifted her lips, seeking another kiss.

It was exactly what Hans Ostfield had directed her to do, a flawless depiction of a young woman's reaction to her first taste of temptation. But Ariel wasn't acting. She was *reacting*, responding instinctively to the man who held her—and to her own pounding blood.

"Come for a ride with me," Zeke murmured. "We'll go swimming at that beach over on the west side of the lake I told you about." He nuzzled her mouth with his, not quite giving her the kiss she craved. "Cool off."

Swimming? Cool off? Ariel tried to think. "I..." What was the line she was supposed to say? "I..."

"Think how good the water will feel," Zeke said, not waiting for her to remember. Stepping all over her lines. "All cool and silky against your skin." He pressed another teasing kiss to her lips, silently coaxing her to say yes.

She was just on the verge of it, just on the end of forgetting all the reasons why she shouldn't even be with him now, let alone go swimming at some secluded beach with him. He was arrogant and oversexed and...

"Come with me, Laura."

Laura?

Ariel's heated little fantasy burst like a bubble. Zeke wasn't holding *her*, kissing *her*, trying to coax *her* into giving in to temptation. It was Judd holding Laura; Judd kissing Laura; Judd whispering sweet tempting words that had been written by someone else for him to say to Laura.

Ariel felt her cheeks heat with embarrassment. She stiffened in Zeke's arms.

He tightened his hold on her. "Come with me," he said again.

"I...I don't have my bathing suit," Ariel stammered, belatedly remembering her line.

"That's all right. I won't look. I promise. I'll turn my back until you're in the water." He kissed the corner of her mouth again. "Say yes, Laura."

"I..." She squeezed her eyes shut and prayed for the courage to see the scene through when all she wanted to do was run and hide. "Yes," she said and pressed her lips to his, playing it exactly as it had been written in the script.

She held the final kiss like the trooper she was, her arms around Zeke's neck, her breasts flattened against his chest, her nerves screaming with tension and embarrassment, waiting for the director's indication that he'd gotten everything he wanted from the scene. It seemed to be taking forever.

"And . . . cut," Hans said, finally. "Print it."

Zeke stood up and thrust her away from him with his hands at her waist. "For Crissake, Princess, next time try to remember your lines," he snarled, and brushed past her as if he couldn't get away fast enough.

Ariel stood there for a shocked moment, blinking back hot, confused tears and hoping no one had noticed. Not his inexplicable rudeness, nor her own brief, embarrassing lapse into the fantasy they'd been creating for the camera.

THEY'D FILMED the love scene at the lake less than a month later, in the man-made pond on one of the studio's back lots. It had gone much more smoothly, with no forgotten lines and no embarrassment except for what an eighteen-year-old girl might normally be expected to feel at being asked to surrender the top of her bathing suit once she'd gotten into the water with a film crew as witnesses.

It would look better for the cameras, Hans had said, enhancing the illusion that Laura had succumbed to Judd's blandishments and was swimming naked. She'd hesitated at first but the water was murky and no one would really see anything—and Zeke had challenged her by taking his trunks off underwater and flinging them onto the shore.

After the first three takes, Ariel almost forgot she was topless beneath the water. She played the scene over and over, as many times as Hans asked her to, beautifully. She was shy and giggly one minute, bold and flirtatious the next, as Laura and Judd played a teasing game of sexual retreat and advance. And when it came time for her to surrender herself to his embrace, she went easily, naturally, into his arms, letting him press her bare breasts to his chest, his bare belly to hers, while he cupped her head in his hands and kissed her senseless. She remembered feeling his erection, pressed against her stomach under the water, but there was no fear, no maidenly shock or revulsion. They were lovers by then, and she was used to his hands and his mouth and the feel of his lean hard body. Used to the heat they created in her....

ARIEL ROLLED OVER in the water with a low moan, feeling that heat again—*still!*—and dived toward the bottom of the pool in an effort to alleviate it. But the coolness she sought was just an illusion, temporary at best, and the heat inside her was soul deep. She swam to the edge of the pool and levered herself out of the water in one smooth motion.

There was only one way to deal with the pain and the memories, to dissipate the heat. Work. Hard work and lots of it. Maybe it was time to take a long, serious look at one of those movie scripts her agent was always trying to tempt her with. Or maybe she'd see how much clout she really had with the studio heads and suggest the idea for a documentary-style series on women entrepreneurs she'd been thinking about; they'd been trying to entice her to come back to prime-time TV ever since she'd walked away from *Maggie and Me* in its sixth successful season.

Or, hell, she thought recklessly, bending over to pick up her nightgown on her way back into the house, maybe she'd just take a lover. She'd had enough offers over the years. Just that afternoon, one of the young hotshot executives at Gavino Cosmetics had made it more than clear he was interested, if she was.

Maybe she'd take him up on it. Someone young, handsome and virile might just be able to keep her too busy to even *think* about Zeke Blackstone, let alone break her heart over him again.

4

WITH HER USUAL good taste, manic efficiency and attention to detail, Zeke's secretary had apartment 1-G painted and cleaned and ready for him to move into two days after Jack and Faith Shannon moved out. She'd gone with vintage Mission furniture against a soothing color scheme of sand, sage green and dusty sunset shades of peach and aqua that perfectly suited the building's mood and architecture. She'd turned the smallest of the two bedrooms into an efficient high-tech office with three phone lines, a fax machine and a computer system, complete with laser printer. There was a Nordic Track in a corner of the bedroom for his morning workouts and the refrigerator was stocked with Evian, imported light beer and a selection of good-for-you snacks and frozen low-fat gourmet meals. She'd had sturdy new locks installed on the doors and windows, supplemented by a sophisticated alarm system that was controlled by a keypad in the bedroom. Everything was rented—from the expensive designer furniture in the rooms, to the art on the walls, to colorful Fiesta ware in the kitchen, to the alarm system—and everything would be gone two days after Zeke moved out again.

And, yet, it felt lived in and familiar. Almost eerily so, Zeke thought, as if the former occupants had left little bits and pieces of themselves behind. Without even closing his eyes, Zeke could see flashes of his past in the apartment. Ethan Roberts was there, leaning negligently against a doorjamb with a beer in his hand, as smooth and suave as if he were posing for an ad in *GQ*; Eric and Jack Shannon were wrangling over something the way they often did that summer; and the women, dozens of them, beautiful, interchangeable and always available in that long-ago era of free love and uninhibited sex. He could see the little Russian makeup artist, Natasha Kuryan, who'd lived on the first floor, fussing around in the kitchen as she fixed a pot of borscht or some of her special Azerbaijan pilaf so that he and his roommates "shouldn't starve" from their own cooking. And there, too, was Ariel, standing in the middle of the living room, just as she had been at eighteen. Lovely, fragile, innocent Ariel.

From the first time he'd seen her on the studio sound stage, something in her spoke to something in him. Stirred and provoked and challenged him somehow. He'd taken one look at her—America's sweetheart, the fresh-scrubbed princess of prime-time television—and immediately decided to see if he could outwit the dragon who protected her and scale the walls of her castle.

Part of it was that she'd irked him at first, a little, with her old-fashioned innocence and her grave good manners. It had to be a put-on. Nobody was *that* innocent anymore, he'd thought, not in 1970, and certainly not anyone who'd grown up in Hollywood during the turbulent sixties, where "sex, drugs and rock 'n' roll" was the rule rather than the exception.

But Ariel was.

He'd known it for sure the very first time he'd kissed her.

They'd been on the set, under the hot lights and the watchful eyes of Hans Ostfield and the rest of the crew. The cameras were rolling and she was supposed to be acting a part. But she wasn't. Her hesitation and uncertainty had been real. And so had her artless surrender. She'd gotten adorably flustered and stumbled over her lines. And he'd gotten a hard-on that almost burst the buttons on his jeans. He'd pushed her away from him the second the scene was over and said something rude to cover his own confusion and embarrassment before stalking away from the set like James Dean on a tear.

After that, she'd become less of a challenge and more of a . . . cause. He hadn't wanted to storm the walls of her castle anymore, he'd wanted to coax her to come down on her own. He'd wanted to free her from her prison of stifling propriety. It was, after all, 1970, the era of women's liberation and free love, and she was still trapped back in the white-gloved fifties when good girls sat on the sidelines and waited patiently to be asked.

He was an observant young man and it hadn't taken him long to decide *why* Ariel was the way she was. He only had to look as far as her mother. And he didn't like what he saw.

Constance Cameron was a would-be actress with little talent of her own, who'd apparently discovered, early on, that her young fatherless daughter was talented enough for both of them. Constance had given up her own dreams of stardom and concentrated on her daughter's career. Ariel had been working steadily from the age of four, first in commercials and then in primetime television. She'd never gone to a regular school with other children, but had been tutored by her mother between takes. Her mother was also her manager, her agent, her acting coach, wardrobe and script consultant, as well as constant companion, both on the set and off.

Until *Wild Hearts*.

For the first time in her career—and, perhaps, her life—Ariel was out from under her mother's watchful eye.

And smack-dab under the admiring gaze of an experienced hot-eyed young man.

And so, using all his considerable bad-boy charm and the expertise gained in twenty-two years of living, Zeke had begun a determined effort to lure the sheltered young actress into his arms—and into his bed—for real....

"IT'S ALL RIGHT, sweetheart. You can come in. None of the guys are here."

"Are you sure?"

"Sure, I'm sure," Zeke said, drawing Ariel into the apartment as he spoke. "They've all got day jobs now. Even Ethan," he added, knowing that Ariel didn't like him very much. "He got that part on *As Time Goes By,* the one he auditioned for a couple of weeks ago? He says it looks like it might develop into a regular gig."

"How wonderful for him," she said politely. "He must be pleased about it."

"Yeah, I guess..." He had no desire to talk about any of his roommates or their careers, not when he finally had Ariel alone in his apartment, away from the cast and crew on the set—and her interfering mother. "Here, why don't you take off your sunglasses and that silly scarf?" He reached out to remove the oversize sunglasses and untie the yellow-and-white print Pucci scarf from under her chin. "I don't think anybody's going to recognize you now."

"No, I guess not," Ariel agreed shyly, looking down as he removed the offending items.

"Much better," he said approvingly, and bent to press a quick kiss on her lips.

She looked up, startled, but he had already turned away to place the glasses and scarf on the coffee table.

"Let me put some music on and then I'll get us something to drink. You like Creedence Clearwater?" he asked as he thumbed through the albums stacked upright in the bookshelf. He glanced back over his shoulder when she didn't answer.

She was standing in the middle of the haphazardly decorated living room looking like a shy little daffodil in a sleeveless yellow Givenchy minidress. It had white piping on all the edges and big, oversize white buttons down the front. Her stockings were sheer white, her shoes were yellow patent leather, ankle-strapped wedgies, and she had a wide white-and-yellow polka-dot bangle on one slender wrist. Something about the way she stood and the wary expression in her big blue eyes made Zeke think of a young deer who was on the verge of bolting into the safety of the woods.

He put the album on and hurried back over to her, snagging an arm around her waist as he headed for the kitchen. He turned her sideways as they went through the narrow door, shouldering his way through the multicolored strands of beads that hung from the header.

"Pretty slim pickings," he said when he opened the refrigerator. "I've got Coke or orange soda." There was a bottle of wine, too, but he didn't offer that. He didn't want her to be able to say, later, that she hadn't known what she was doing. "Which will it be?"

"Coke, I guess."

"Two Cokes." He reached into the refrigerator and snagged the bottles by the neck. Resting first one, then the other, firmly against the edge of the counter, he rapped the neck of each bottle with the heel of his hand and popped off the caps. "Do you want a glass?"

Ariel shook her head. "The bottle's fine."

Zeke grinned. "Good choice. I don't think any of the glasses are particularly clean. Jack's on KP this week," he said, reaching past her to hold aside the strands of beads that filled the doorway. "After you."

Ariel smiled nervously and sidled past him. The beads fell back into place as he followed her into the living room. "Sit down?" he invited, gesturing toward the sagging madras-covered sofa.

"Okay," she said softly and sat down, smack-dab on the middle cushion.

Zeke smiled to himself. It was a signal. If she was thinking of changing her mind, she'd have chosen one of the beanbag chairs or sat on one of the end cushions of the sofa. But the middle... that left him plenty of room on either side of her. He put his unwanted Coke on the coffee table, sat down next to her and put his arm around her shoulders.

She shot him a quick, nervous look out of the corner of her eye and then looked back down at the bottle of soda clutched between her hands. But she didn't move away.

He bent his head and kissed her bare shoulder.

She took a tiny sip of her soda and refused to look at him.

He ran his fingertip down her arm.

She shivered, tightening her grasp on the bottle, but still wouldn't look at him.

He transferred his touch to her knee, running his fingertips lightly, delicately, up the top of her white-stockinged thigh to the hem of her little yellow dress and back down again.

She gasped and closed her eyes. And didn't move.

"Ariel?"

"What?"

"Are you afraid?"

"No," she lied.

"Have you changed your mind?"

"No."

"Then would you look at me, please?"

Slowly, shyly, she turned her head against his arm and looked at him. Her blue eyes were wide and wondering and just a little bit frightened, despite what she'd said.

"You know I won't hurt you, don't you?" Zeke whispered.

"I know," she whispered back.

"We'll go slow. As slow as you want. And we'll stop whenever you say," he promised. "You don't ever have to be afraid of me."

"I'm not. Really." She smiled tremulously, trying to reassure him. "I'm just a little nervous, is all."

"So am I," Zeke admitted.

That seemed to surprise and please her. "Really? Why?"

"I've never made love to a virgin before. What if I mess it up for you? Or do something you don't like?"

"I don't know what I like yet. Except when you kiss me," she hinted, emboldened by his admission of vulnerability. "I like that."

Zeke felt something in his gut tighten. "Are you going to drink that Coke?"

In answer, Ariel leaned forward and placed it on the coffee table next to his. And then she leaned back against his arm and tilted her face up to his, inviting his kiss.

Zeke reached up, his hand trembling slightly, and brushed back the soft blond hair at her temple. "You're incredible, do you know that?" he said softly, awed by the trust she'd placed in him just by being there. He knew it couldn't have been easy for her. "Incredibly sweet." He threaded his fingers through the silken length of her hair, lifting it away from her head and letting it drift back down, a few strands at a time. "Incredibly beautiful. I think I'm falling in love with you."

"You don't have to say that." Her voice was soft and sweet, her eyes wide and serious. "I don't want you to pretend to feel something you don't."

"I'm not pretending," he said truthfully, a little stunned to hear himself say it. "I really do think I'm in love with you."

"Really?" she breathed.

"Really," he said and bent his head to kiss her.

She opened her mouth for him immediately, exactly the way she'd learned to in their stolen moments on the set. He claimed it with his tongue, gently teasing hers, trying to beguile her into making demands of her own. But she was acquiescent and shy, still unused to physical intimacy, and he couldn't wait for her to respond more emphatically. He deepened his possession of her mouth, leaning over her, pressing her head back against his encircling arm, letting his free hand drift down the side of her face and her shoulder to lightly, lightly cover her breast.

Ariel sighed against his lips and lifted her arm to encircle his neck, pulling herself closer and tacitly giving him permission to go further. Zeke took what she offered, cupping his fingers around her breast to test its weight and contour. He brushed his thumb back and forth over the tip, seeking the nipple through the thick layer of yellow cotton piqué and the fabric of her bra. Finding it, he circled it gently, plucking at it with his fingertips until she moaned and arched against his hand.

"I think we found something else you like," he murmured, his voice rich with satisfaction and pleasure. He loosened his hold on her a bit, letting his fingers drift to the row of big white buttons running down the front of her dress. "You might like it even more if we opened these."

There was a moment's silence and then she said softly, "Okay," and he could feel her lips move against his neck.

He shifted against her eagerly, needing to use both hands to slip the oversize buttons from their buttonholes. "Lift your head a little, sweetheart, so I can see what I'm doing here," he instructed, using the back of one hand to brush a thick sheaf of her waist-length hair out of the way as he spoke.

And Ariel obediently lifted her head, making it easier for him to get at her buttons. "I think I'm in love with you, too," she blurted.

Zeke looked up, arrested in midmotion, his hands still busy with her buttons. "You don't have to say that, either, you know," he told her. "It isn't required."

"No, I mean it," Ariel said. "I think I . . . that is, I've never felt this way before. My heart's pounding so hard and it hurts to breathe and . . ."

He smiled. "It might not be love, you know, sweetheart," he warned her. "It might just be sex." *And a little bit of fear mixed in*, he thought.

Ariel blushed and looked away.

Zeke put his hand under her chin, turning her face back to his. "Sex is okay, Ariel. No matter what anyone's told you before. Sex is healthy and natural."

"Even without love?"

"Sure, even without love. I'm not saying you should do this with just anyone," he added quickly, just in case she misunderstood and thought he was giving her free rein. "You should care about the person. A lot. A whole lot," he emphasized. "But you don't have to be in love." He leaned forward and kissed her, then let her go to finish with the buttons. "I've heard it's better when you're in love but I wouldn't know from personal experience." He looked up suddenly and grinned. "Maybe I'll find out today, huh?"

"Maybe we'll both—" she began but he was no longer listening.

The buttons down the front of her dress were all undone and he pushed the two halves of the yellow piqué fabric aside to reveal what lay beneath. She was long and lean and exquisite under her expensive, fashionable clothes. Her breasts were small and conical beneath her white lace bra. Her hips were narrow, the rounded bones on either side prominent beneath the sheer white fabric of her panty hose. The downy mound at the juncture of her thighs was covered by a swatch of white lace no bigger than a handkerchief. He cupped his hands around her small breasts, lifting them, and bent his head to kiss the cleavage he'd created. Ariel stiffened and lifted her hands to his hair, sinking her fingers into the thick, shaggy curls to hold him there.

They stayed like that for a sweet endless moment— Zeke with his mouth pressed against the fragile skin between her breasts, and Ariel with her hands fisted in his hair and her eyes closed. Then he raised his head and she opened her eyes and they smiled at each other.

"I think we'd better take this into the bedroom," Zeke suggested softly. He stood and held out his hand to her. "We'll be more comfortable in there."

She put her hand trustingly in his and let him pull her to her feet. Then, one hand holding the front of her dress closed, she walked with him into the bedroom.

There were two double beds, one pushed against each wall, with a folding Chinese paper screen partially opened between them. The side of the room Zeke led her to was at least nominally neat. The bed was made, with a plain navy blue blanket and white percale cases on the pillows. A pierced-brass Indian drum table sat beside it, holding a single lamp and a paperback book. Two framed vintage movie posters graced the otherwise bare walls above the bed.

Letting go of her hand, Zeke hurriedly grabbed up the rumpled clothes lying in a heap on the floor and tossed them into the wicker chest at the foot of his bed, then pulled the paper screen out to its full length, hiding the messy other half of the room from view. The textured paper screen filtered the light coming in through the single uncurtained window, softening it to a gentle dappled glow, like sunlight shining through water.

While Zeke tidied the room, Ariel sat down on the edge of his bed and removed her shoes. Setting them neatly aside, she stood and reached for the waistband of her panty hose. She stopped suddenly, pausing with the fabric pushed down around her hips, and looked up at him with a shy smile. "Don't watch," she said.

And Zeke tore his fascinated gaze away and turned around, giving her his back. He could hear her rustling around behind him and imagined each garment slipping from her body; the gossamer sheer panty hose as she pushed them down her long legs; the expensive designer dress as she slipped it off her shoulders; the white lace bra as she reached behind her to unfasten it; the delicate swatch of fabric that shielded her woman's secrets. And then he heard the quick flurry of her bare feet against the hardwood floor and the squeak of the bedsprings.

"You can look now," she said breathlessly.

And he turned to see her snuggled down in his bed with her glorious hair spread out on his pillow and the navy blue blanket pulled up to her chin. She'd folded her dress over the wicker trunk at the foot of the bed, her panty hose and underwear tucked modestly out of sight beneath it.

Without a word, he reached up behind him, grabbed a handful of his T-shirt and yanked it off over his head. Dropping it carelessly on the floor, he propped one foot, and then the other, on the edge of the bed to remove his tan suede desert boots. They each hit the floor with a thud. Zeke straightened and reached for the button fly front of his bell-bottom jeans. Ariel watched, fascinated, as he slowly popped each metal button in turn. And he watched her watch, his gaze on her face, drinking in her innocent fascination. And then he tucked his thumbs into the waistband of his jeans.

Ariel squeezed her eyes shut.

"You can look," Zeke said, his voice a low growl. "I want you to."

Ariel opened her eyes a tiny crack, peeking at him through her lashes as he pushed his jeans and Jockey shorts down his narrow hips. She gasped as his erection sprang free, and her eyes opened wide.

Zeke grinned, pleased by her reaction. "Don't look so scared, sweetheart. It'll fit. I promise." He reached for the corner of the blanket, then paused, remembering one more thing that had to be taken care of before he climbed into bed beside her. "Are you on the Pill?"

Ariel flushed with embarrassment. "No, I . . . ah . . ."

"It's all right," he assured her. "I didn't think you were but I wanted to make sure. I'll take care of it." And then he lifted the blankets and slid into bed beside her.

Her body was cool and slim as he took her into his arms. Her mouth was warm and eager beneath his. There were shy hesitations and excited exclamations at each new stage of their lovemaking. She stayed his hand when he first moved to pull the covers down to her waist and then, a few moments later, she pushed the blankets away herself as he burrowed beneath them to caress her breasts with his mouth. She pressed her legs together at the first tentative touch of his fingers, and then sighed and let her thighs fall open as he gently rubbed his palm against her woman's mound.

Soon she was moving against his hand, her head turning restlessly on the pillow, her back arched as she searched for that elusive something that hovered just beyond her reach. Zeke worked his fingers between her slender thighs, delicately circling the entrance to her body, dipping into her growing moistness to lubricate the little nub of flesh that throbbed to his touch. He could feel her climax approaching, could tell by the way she unconsciously stiffened her body and the panting little cries that came from deep in her throat, that she was balancing on the knife-edge of the ultimate pleasure. He inserted two fingers into her, deeply, and spread them wide, at the same time pressing his thumb against her clitoris. She plummeted over the edge with a ragged cry, exploding into passionate release like a rocket.

Zeke held her tight while she rode it out and then lifted himself over her body, settling his hips between her thighs, pressing the engorged head of his condom-sheathed penis against the moist, swollen folds of her untried body.

Ariel moaned and lifted her hips, instinctively offering herself for his most intimate possession.

Zeke groaned and clenched his hands against the sheets, reminding himself of the importance of taking things slowly, of treating her gently, especially now. "Ariel," he murmured, his voice guttural with need and the terrible strain of holding back, when what he wanted to do was plunge himself into her to the hilt. "Ariel, sweetheart, open your eyes and look at me."

Ariel complied, slowly, lifting her lashes to reveal eyes made even more intensely blue with the heat of her passion.

"This might hurt a little," he warned her in a gritty whisper. "Tell me if it hurts too much and I'll . . . I'll try to stop."

"I don't want you to stop. Ever," she said fiercely, and lifted her legs to wrap them around his hips.

He sank into her with a ragged moan. She gasped softly and stiffened but her arms and legs were tight around him and her face was pressed into the curve of his neck. "Don't stop," she whispered, urging him on with the instinctive undulation of her slim hips. He gave in to her urging then, mindlessly driving toward his own release, unaware that she achieved a second explosive climax as he exploded into his own burning version of sublime ecstasy.

And, later, when they were both calmer and breathing more normally, Zeke lifted his head and looked down into her shining, worshipful eyes. "It *is* better when you're in love," he whispered, awestruck.

5

"DINNER'S GOING TO BE a little earlier than you're used to, Dad," Cameron warned him several days later, having tracked him down via telephone.

"How early?"

"Six. Michael's parents drove up from La Jolla this afternoon and they're driving back tonight. And Michael's on the night shift at the hospital for the next month because he's pulling double duty to make up for the two weeks he's taking off for our honeymoon. So he's going to have to leave early, too. Mom said to tell everyone that she'll be serving the hors d'oeuvres at precisely five-thirty."

"Precisely, huh?" Zeke said sourly.

"Precisely." Cameron mimicked his tone. "So don't be late, okay?"

"Jeez, a guy's late one lousy time and—"

Two soft clicks sounded in his ear.

"That's my other line," Cameron said. "Gotta go, Dad. I'll see you tonight. Bye."

Zeke couldn't help but grin as he placed the receiver of the phone back into the cradle. Cameron had always been a bundle of energy, none of it suppressed. Even as a little girl, she'd invariably had three or four projects going at once. She was very much his daughter in that respect; he always had his fingers in half a dozen different pies, too. She'd gotten her eyes from him, as well, and a certain determined set about her chin. But the rest had come directly from Ariel; the pale gold hair, the delicate bone structure, the instinctive tact and diplomacy.

Mom said to tell everyone that she'll be serving the hors d'oeuvres at precisely five-thirty.

He'd bet the gross receipts from his next picture deal that Ariel hadn't said anything of the kind. *Tell your father not to be late again* was probably closer to the truth.

He had half a mind to call his ex-wife up and tell her to deliver her messages herself from now on, except that he knew it wouldn't do any good. She'd be exquisitely polite, exceedingly gracious and subtly disdainful, like a maître d' at a very trendy restaurant dealing with some epicurean philistine who'd had the audacity to complain about the food—all of which would put him squarely in the wrong without her having to utter a word of condemnation. That was supposing he even got her on the phone, of course. Ariel had always had a whole phalanx of people insulating her from the ill-mannered riffraff inhabiting the outside world, starting with her mother. Now there was her housekeeper Eleanor, her secretary, her lawyer, her agent and who knew who else.

In the last twenty-five years, Zeke doubted he'd spoken to Ariel directly more than a handful of times—and one of those times had been when they'd exchanged vows at their wedding. The announcement of his daughter's birth had come through a high-priced celebrity lawyer, three days after the fact and in the same plain manila envelope that had been used to serve him with the divorce papers. And hidden among all the legal mumbo jumbo had been a one-paragraph clause stating that he was voluntarily giving up all custody rights to his newborn daughter. . . .

"IT'S COMPLETELY out of the question. Completely! Dammit, I'm *not* giving up my daughter!" Zeke shouted, slamming his fist against the wall for emphasis. It made the framed New England seascapes hanging behind the lawyer's desk quiver on their hooks. "What the hell kind of man does she think I am?"

"The kind, apparently," the lawyer suggested, "who wouldn't think twice about giving up custody of a daughter he's never seen. It says here—" he indicated the documents on the desk in front of him "—that you haven't shown any interest in the child, either before or after her birth."

"That's been Ariel's doing, not mine. Ariel's and her mother's," Zeke said bitterly. "I would have been right by her side through the whole thing, beginning to end, if I'd had any say in it. And I tried to see the baby as soon as I found out she'd been born, but they wouldn't even let me in the front door. They've got her in a private clinic and my name isn't on the list of approved visitors. I'm her father, dammit! I have a right to see my daughter." The look he turned on the lawyer was almost pleading. "Don't I?"

"Yes, of course. As the child's father you have a legal right to see her."

"But?" Zeke demanded, fearing from the lawyer's expression that there had to be a *but*.

"You and your wife have been estranged since shortly after you were married, according to what your agent told me when she called to set up this appointment. Is that correct?"

Reluctantly Zeke nodded. The estrangement had started well before the wedding but if Ariel and her mother wanted to pretend it had come after, he would let them. As long as doing so didn't interfere with his right to see his daughter.

"Then is it also correct to assume that you only married Miss Cameron to legitimize the child she was carrying?"

"No, that is *not* correct," Zeke said firmly, his tone harsh. He thought he saw where his line of questioning was going now and he didn't like it. "I asked Ariel to marry me before I knew she was pregnant. And then I asked her again after I found out about the baby. She was the one who—" He stopped abruptly.

Even now, after everything, he couldn't betray her, or say anything that might put her in a bad light. He was as much to blame for the sorry mess their lives were in as she was. More really. Four years her senior, he was older and, supposedly, wiser. He should have been more patient and understanding of her fears and uncertainties. Less hotheaded and demanding. Maybe things would have worked out differently.

"This is all confidential, isn't it?" he asked. "You can't repeat anything I tell you to anyone unless I say so, right?"

"Whatever you say to me is protected by client-lawyer privilege. It goes no further than this room."

"All right." Zeke sighed and pushed both hands through his hair, thinking how best to explain what had happened when, in truth, he only half understood it all himself. "Ariel and I met last summer while we were filming *Wild Hearts* and we—" *fell in love, I thought* "—got involved. It turned out we were all wrong for each other." He gave a harsh bark of humorless laughter. "Ariel's mother was right on about that," he admitted. "Anyway, just about the time everything was falling apart, Ariel found out she was pregnant. She felt . . . trapped, is the best way to describe it, I guess." At least, that was the way Ariel's mother had described Ariel's feelings to him; Ariel had refused to speak to him about it at all. "But she finally agreed that getting married was the only way to avoid a big scandal."

"Scandal over an out-of-wedlock pregnancy? In this day and age? In Hollywood?"

"Yeah, well . . . Can't have America's reigning sweetheart becoming an unwed mother, now can we?" Zeke said sarcastically. "According to her mother, people might still talk some and count the months, but once we were married, who'd really care? It'd be old news by then. The baby would have a name and Ariel's career wouldn't be adversely affected by bad publicity because she'd have already done the right thing by marrying the father of her child." He shrugged. "Lots of people sleep together before the wedding date so it's no big deal. And we agreed—" Ariel and her mother had *insisted*, actually, and he had gone along with it because he couldn't see what else to do "—that after the wedding we'd both go our separate ways and, after the baby was born, she'd initiate divorce proceedings."

"And when you made this agreement, was giving up your parental rights part of it?"

"No, never. We *never* discussed the possibility that I might give up the right to be a father to my child. In fact, I distinctly remembering telling Ariel's mother—" but not Ariel because she had cut off all direct communication with him "—that I fully intended to be part of my child's life."

The lawyer nodded and made a note on the yellow legal pad in front of him. "Is there anything in your background your wife could use to have you declared unfit or dangerous to the well-being of a child?" he asked. "Alcohol or drug abuse, for instance? Bouts of violence? Sexual depravity of some kind?"

"No, nothing," Zeke said firmly. Then added, "Oh, hell, I've smoked pot a few times. Who hasn't? But Ariel wouldn't—"

He broke off, aghast. Ariel might not use it against him but Constance would. And Ariel was sufficiently under her mother's thumb to let her. Well, they wouldn't get away with it.

"I'm that baby's daddy and I intend to stay her daddy," Zeke said passionately. "And if Ariel or her mother wants to fight me on that, then I'll show them scandal," he vowed. "I'll turn America's little sweetheart into a scarlet woman if I have to."

ARIEL HADN'T FOUGHT him on it. Instead, the lawyers had gotten together and hammered out an agreement for joint custody. At first, when Cameron was an infant and still nursing, Zeke was allowed access to the nursery floor of Ariel's Beverly Hills mansion three times a week for an hour at a time.

It was there, in the cheerful yellow-and-white room decorated with checked gingham and gamboling baby farm animals, under the watchful eye of a uniformed nurse, that he'd first held his daughter in his arms. She'd been tiny and bald, with big, dark, serious eyes and a rosebud mouth. She'd stared up at him with owlish intensity, her tiny mouth pursed, her little brow furrowed, as if she were trying to figure out who this new person in her life was. And then, apparently satisfied with whatever she'd seen, she'd trustfully closed her eyes and fallen asleep. And Zeke had fallen irrevocably, completely, utterly in love.

As Cameron grew older and more independent of her mother, Zeke's time with her increased. Hours became full days, and days, weekends, and then entire weeks. With his movie career in full swing after the success of *Wild Hearts*, Zeke bought the beach house in Malibu and had it remodeled to accommodate the needs of a child. He taught Cameron to swim and then to surf in the blue Pacific outside the front door. He learned to braid her hair, helped her with her homework, vetted her boyfriends, disciplined her when she needed it. And he marveled that he and Ariel were somehow managing to raise a happy, well-adjusted, self-confident child—despite the fact that they were never in the same room together and rarely spoke, even on the telephone.

Cameron had apparently accepted the odd arrangement as perfectly normal. It never seemed to bother her that her mother and father took turns attending her school functions or that holidays were alternated, or that she had two homes, each of which ran on different time schedules, with rules and rhythms that were slightly different from those at the other. She accepted with equanimity that, if her date picked her up for the prom at her mother's, then, of course, he had to drive across town so her father could take pictures of her in her prom dress, too. She registered no protest or disappointment when her parents arrived separately at both her high school and college graduations, sat on opposite sides of the auditorium and left without speaking to one another.

Cameron never made a fuss. She never whined or pouted or tried to make her parents feel guilty for the way things were. She had only ever asked that they come together and cooperate for one special function.

Her wedding.

Which is why, Zeke thought, he'd better quit stalling and start getting ready for the evening ahead. After all, how bad could it be, really? Cameron and Michael would be there the whole time. Michael's parents. Eleanor would undoubtedly be on hand to serve dinner. He'd have to endure three, maybe four hours tops, of being politely ignored by his ex-wife. Surely he could restrain himself for that long. Although restrain himself from *what*, he wasn't exactly sure.

He'd already about convinced himself that the feeling he'd felt in the wedding consultants' office couldn't have been what he thought it was. He couldn't still be in love with Ariel after twenty-five years. If, he thought, he'd ever really been in love with her at all. The feelings he'd experienced had been intense and violent at the time, but what hot-blooded twenty-two-year-old male's feelings weren't when it came to women and sex? Especially forbidden women and hot, clandestine sex. No, he wasn't in love with her. Maybe not then. And certainly not now.

He ran his hand through his hair nervously.

No, certainly not now.

It was mostly just the shock of seeing her again, up close and personal, he told himself. Shock and bittersweet memories and—hell, why not just admit it?— plain old testosterone. Not only was Ariel still one of the most beautiful women he'd ever seen, but she'd matured into exactly the kind of woman he found most desirable. He'd always gone for the sleek, subtly sexy type. The ones with a cool edge and a layer of elegance that was more than skin-deep; complicated women, usually, who had standards and opinions and who didn't hesitate to give a man a hard time when he stepped out of line. The kind of woman who used to be called a classy dame, back when being called a dame wasn't considered an insult.

And even back in 1970, when Ariel was just a girl, she'd been classy.

He'd often thought his life would have been a great deal easier if he'd been content with the simple, giggly, wiggly, comfortable sort of woman who only lived to please her man. God knew, that kind of woman was abundant on the Hollywood scene and always had been. And, truth to tell, he'd had relationships with one or two...or three...but they'd never lasted very long. He'd confused them and hurt their feelings; and they'd bored him to tears. Like an acting role or a business deal—or life, itself—a woman didn't interest him for long if she didn't present a challenge.

And that's *exactly* what the attraction was now, he told himself. That was *all* it was. Ariel represented a challenge. She was the classiest of the classy dames; the cool, unassailable lady of the manor; the one who got away. The blow he had felt at seeing her again hadn't been to his heart at all, but to his pride.

Well, he was wasn't going to do anything to assuage that wounded pride, he told himself sternly. No, sir. He wasn't some raw, cocky kid anymore, hell-bent on proving his manhood. He was a responsible adult, a father, and he was going to behave. He wasn't going to stir up trouble by trying to charm his ex-wife back into his bed just to prove to them both that he still could.

With that thought firmly in mind, he glanced at his watch then reached for the telephone again. He had time to make a few calls, he thought, tie up a couple of loose ends on his current project, get the ball rolling a little faster on his next one. Immersing himself in his work had always been his way of staying out of trouble. Or, more usually, avoiding *more* trouble. Trouble that invariably involved a woman somewhere along the line.

Two days after his farce of a wedding to Ariel, he'd started work on his second picture for Universal Studios. The movie had premiered the same week he received the Oscar nomination as Best Actor for *Wild Hearts*, imprinting his reputation as a hot young stud in the public consciousness and cementing his career as an actor. He'd taken his first shot at directing when his second marriage—to a brilliant and beautiful entertainment lawyer—started to fall apart, less than two years after the wedding. He'd bitten the bullet and started his own production company three weeks after the actress he'd been living with on and off for six months sued him for palimony. A thriving career didn't exactly make up for a tangled love life, but it helped. Some.

It was also about to make him late. Again.

It was a quarter to five when he finally concluded his business and hung up the phone. With a muffled curse, he dashed to the bathroom, showered, shaved and dressed in record time, racing out of the apartment like a schoolboy who'd already missed the first bell. He hurried through the small front lobby, pushing open the door without looking, and almost knocked down the woman who was just coming in.

"Excuse me," he muttered, automatically catching her by the elbows to steady her without really seeing her. He was going to be late and Ariel was going to give him one of those censorious, well-bred looks that could make a man feel as if he were a scruffy little boy who'd tracked mud all over her spotless pastel carpets. "I'm sorry. I—"

"Ezekiel?" The woman held onto his forearms when he would have politely put her away from him. "Ezekiel Blackstone?"

Zeke couldn't believe his ears. Only one person besides his mother had ever called him that. Her hair was snowy white, her soft, pale skin was lined with age, her full gypsy skirts, high-necked antique-lace blouse and fringed paisley shawl were from another time, but her sparkling green eyes were still as clear and bright as a young girl's. It was amazing; she'd looked exactly the same the last time he'd seen her, nearly twenty-five years ago.

His politely distracted smile changed to one of real pleasure; he'd always had a soft spot for the eccentric little woman. "Madame Kuryan."

"My stars, it *is* you," she said, her faint Russian accent still discernible after who knew how many years in the United States. "You are the mysterious new tenant in 1-G? The one Superintendent Amberson would say nothing about?"

"Temporarily. Until the repairs on my house are finished."

"How very strange. You know that young Jack Shannon and his lovely wife have just moved out of that apartment?" she asked, her eyes bright with curiosity.

"I know. Quite a coincidence, isn't it?"

"It is destiny," she said firmly, with an emphatic nod of her head. "Kismet. You were meant to come back."

He shrugged that away and took her hands in his. "I can't believe *you're* still here after all these years."

She lifted one shoulder in an eloquent shrug. "You thought such an old lady would be dead by now, hmm? Part of the legend of the Bachelor Arms, maybe?"

Zeke laughed and raised her hands to his lips. "Not old, Madame," he said, and kissed each one in turn. "Ageless."

Natasha Kuryan glowed. "You were always the most charming of the boys. He was a devil with the ladies, this one," she said, turning to the young woman Zeke only just now noticed standing behind her. "He is still a devil, I think," she added, her green eyes twinkling flirtatiously. "A swashbuckler like my Errol."

"I'm honored to be in such exalted company," Zeke said, knowing she was referring the late Errol Flynn. Rumor had it that Madame Kuryan, once a makeup artist to the biggest Hollywood stars, and the famous movie actor had been quite an item back in the late forties. It was a rumor Zeke had no trouble believing; judging by the pictures he'd seen, Natasha Kuryan had been an spectacularly beautiful woman in her prime. She still was, as far as Zeke was concerned.

"If I was forty years younger, I might be tempted to tame myself a devil, just once more." She flashed another glance over her shoulder at the young woman behind her. "To show these young girls how it is done," she teased, and then laughed softly and shook her head. "But I am an old woman now, so I will leave all these silly modern girls to figure it out on their own." She turned and motioned the young woman forward. "This is my young friend Bobbie-Sue O'Hara," she said, introducing her to Zeke. "She is a very good actress. You would be wise to put her in one of your films."

Zeke reached out to shake the young woman's hand, pretending not to notice her embarrassment at the old woman's bluntness. "I was wondering where I'd seen you before," he said. "You had a small part in that miniseries on TV last Fall. *Bitter Harvest*, wasn't it?"

"A very small part," Bobbie-Sue said, obviously both amazed and pleased that he'd recognized her.

"But very effective." Zeke's eyes narrowed a bit as he studied her. She was young and beautiful, with soft blond hair and big blue eyes that managed to be both sweet and cynical at the same time. He made one of his lightning-quick business decisions. "I'm in the middle of casting a new movie." He reached into the inside pocket of his jacket as he spoke and pulled out a business card and a plain gold pen. Quickly, he scribbled something on the back of the card. "That's my casting director's name and number," he said, as he handed it to her. The pen disappeared back into his pocket. "Have your agent call and set up an appointment. I'd like you to read for the part of Kimberly."

Bobbie-Sue's big blue eyes got even bigger. "Mr. Blackstone," she breathed, looking back and forth between him and the card in her hand. "I don't know what to say. I—" She struggled to get hold of herself. "Thank you."

"It's just a reading," he said, feeling compelled to warn her. "It may not lead to anything."

"Yes, of course. I realize that. I had an audition with Xanadu Studio once and didn't get the part," she said. "But thank you for the opportunity just the same."

Natasha Kuryan was almost as delighted as Bobbie-Sue at the turn of events. Her soft, lined old face beamed her approval. "We are going to feed the parrot in 2-C." She shook her head. "That apartment gets the most unusual tenants. And then I have invited Bobbie-Sue to have supper in my apartment and look at my scrapbooks of old Hollywood, when it was still glamorous. We would be pleased if you would join us. We are having my special *pirozhki* and cabbage soup," she added, as if to entice him.

"I'd love to," Zeke said, meaning it. "But I'm afraid I'll have to take a rain check. I'm already late for an appointment."

BOTH OF MICHAEL'S parents were doctors. His father was in private practice in La Jolla. His mother was a research scientist at the Scripps Institute in San Diego. They were both thrilled with their son's prospective bride—and a little nervous about meeting her two famous parents. But Zeke's good-natured, I'm-just-one-of-the-guys grin, combined with Ariel's unparalleled abilities as a hostess, put them immediately at ease. Soon they were sitting around the dinner table, talking like old friends.

"Michael told us how you two met," Sondra Everett said to Cameron as they lingered over coffee and after-dinner liqueurs. "I thought it sounded like the perfect way for a doctor to meet his future wife. Very romantic."

Cameron smiled across the table at her future mother-in-law. "Well, I don't know how romantic it was. One of the secretaries at the office almost sliced her thumb off with an X-Acto knife and I took her to the emergency room for stitches. Michael was on duty." She transferred her smile to her fiancé, looking at him as if he were Sir Lancelot and young Dr. Kildare rolled into one. "He asked me for a date while he was stitching her up. I was so flustered and impressed I said yes before I stopped to think about it."

Michael's father slapped his son on the shoulder. "Quick work, son," he said with a wink.

"Well, I *had* to ask her out," Michael said, adding his own two cents to the story. "She stood there with blood all over the front of her blouse, cool as a seasoned surgical nurse, while I stitched that girl's thumb." His easy grin flashed and he reached out to cover Cameron's hand where it lay on the table between them. "I knew if I didn't ask her out quick, one of those other clowns in the ER would." He shook his head. "You have no idea how hard it is to find a date who doesn't get all squeamish and queasy at the sight of blood and needles. Especially one who looks like Cami."

"Talk about squeamish," Sondra Everett said with a soft laugh. "You should have seen your father the first time he had to cut into a cadaver."

"Now, Sondra," Dan Everett objected mildly. "Mike's heard that story a dozen times."

"His eyes rolled back in his head." Sondra shot her husband a teasing look. "And he just sank to the floor like a stone."

"Is that how you met?" Cameron asked.

Sondra shook her head. "We were assigned to each other as lab partners in our very first biology class at med school."

"And we've been partners ever since," her husband added fondly, in what was obviously an often-voiced sentiment.

Now that's true love, Zeke thought, watching the exchange between his daughter's future in-laws. There

was no apparent strife in their relationship, no histri-
onics or hysterics. Just deep, calm abiding love, the way
love was supposed to be. He'd never had that with Ariel. Their relationship had been fraught with problems
from the very first. His problems. Her problems. Their
problems.

They hadn't come together in any natural sort of
way, meeting and then getting to know each other
gradually. They'd been thrown together, literally, becoming unnaturally intimate before they barely knew
each other well enough to say hello. That very situation regularly wrecked havoc in the lives of any number of adult actors—and he and Ariel had just been a
couple of kids with over-stimulated hormones. It had
been a classic case of opposites attracting—the street-
wise young actor from New York, fresh from a successful off-Broadway play and the sheltered young
television star with a list of credits as long as her arm.
He'd been cocky and full of himself, using bravado to
hide his insecurities. She'd been sweet, shy and curious. When you added the Romeo and Juliet angle pro-
vided by her over-protective dragon of a mother...
Hell, was it any wonder they'd thought they were in
love? And had anybody but the two of them been surprised when it fell apart once the last roll of film was in
the can?

"How did you two first meet?" Dan asked, looking
back and forth between Zeke and Ariel.

Zeke looked up from his contemplation of his brandy
glass in time to see the other man bend down and reach
under the table. Probably to rub the ankle his wife had
just kicked, Zeke thought. But the question had been
asked and it was hanging in the air, waiting to be answered. Zeke looked down the length of the beauti-

fully set table, to where his ex-wife sat at the other end, silently ceding the privilege of answering it to her. Would she remember their first meeting the same way he did?

"We met at work," Ariel said, making it sound as normal and uneventful as a day at the office. "On a soundstage at Universal."

"They were filming *Wild Hearts*," Cameron added, when it appeared that neither Zeke nor Ariel was going to elaborate further. "It was the first movie either of them ever did. Dad got his first Oscar nomination for Best Actor."

"*Wild Hearts?*" Sondra Everett said, apparently forgetting discretion at the prospect of hearing more about the seemingly magical business of making movies. "My goodness, I saw that just last week on American Movie Classics on TV. It's always been one of my favorites. So romantic. And such a romantic way to meet."

"I hate to disillusion you but the romance was all on the screen," Ariel said with an elegant little shrug. "Making it look that way wasn't the least bit romantic at all."

"Oh, come on now, Ariel," Zeke disagreed, irked at her deliberately casual dismissal of what had been between them. "It was a little bit romantic." He flashed his million dollar bad-boy grin at their guests. "Remember the scene in the movie where Laura and Judd first kiss? The one where she comes out of the convenience store and he's sitting outside on his Harley, waiting for her?" The questions were addressed to Sondra Everett but the words were aimed, point blank, at his ex-wife. "It was the very first scene we filmed for the movie. We barely knew each other but Hans—our director, Hans Ostfield, he won an Oscar a couple of years ago for *The Promise?*"

Sondra nodded. "With Tara Channing and Pierce Kingston. I have the video."

"Hans thought shooting that scene first, before we really got to know each other, would give it more authenticity. Capture the nervousness of a first kiss and all. Well, we were nervous, all right. Remember, Ariel?" He shifted his hot, dark-eyed gaze down the length of the table, locking it with that of his ex-wife, staring into her eyes as if they were all alone at the candlelit table. "Things got so . . . romantic—" he said softly, hesitating just long enough for his audience to know that "romantic" wasn't the half of it "—that Ariel muffed her lines. And I . . . well . . ." He shrugged and transferred his gaze back to that of his fascinated listeners. "What happened to me probably isn't fit to talk about in mixed company," he confided with a roguish grin.

Ariel's chair legs squeaked against the tiled marble floor as she pushed back from the table. "It looks like a beautiful night," she said as she rose to her feet. "Shall we finish our drinks out by the pool?"

Her voice was perfectly pleasant, her smile was graciousness itself but the look she shot down the table at her ex-husband could have frozen molten lava.

"Actually, it's time we were going," Sondra Everett said into the small silence that followed her hostess's words. "We have quite a long drive ahead of us, don't we, Dan?"

"Two and a half, three hours, depending on traffic." Dan Everett made a show of looking at his watch. "I had no idea it was so late already."

"I'm afraid I have to be on my way, too." Michael pushed his chair away from the table and stood. "I need to stop by my apartment and change before I head on over to the hospital," he explained with a charming smile. "I'm afraid I'm going to have to drag Cami away, too. We drove over in her car."

There was a general flurry of napkins being laid down and chairs being pushed back and, minutes later, they found themselves at the wide front door of Ariel's Beverly Hills mansion, exchanging the usual round of thank-yous and good-nights.

"It was a great dinner, Mom," Cameron said as she kissed her mother on the cheek. "Tell Eleanor she outdid herself, as usual."

"It's been a lovely evening," Sondra Everett said. "It'll be our turn next time."

"Thank you for coming," Ariel said as she stood in the open doorway, bidding her guests good-night, a gracious hostess to the end. "Drive safely, everyone."

She shut the front door, softly, quietly, one hand on the knob and the other pressed flat against the smooth wood, and then rested her forehead against it for a moment, gathering strength.

She'd thought the evening would never end! And there was still the rehearsal dinner to get through, and the wedding itself. And then the reception, with all its attendant traditions of familial togetherness and co-operation. Thank God, it would all be over soon. In a little less than a month, Cameron and Michael would be married and on their honeymoon, and she could go back to pretending her ex-husband didn't exist. Until then, she'd just have to find a way to deal with his...his overwhelming, unsettling, *unnerving* presence the best way she could.

Pushing away from the door, she turned and walked back through the house, automatically turning off lights as she went, through the foyer and the front parlor, down the hallway to the small informal dining room overlooking the pool area.

She'd intended to clear the table and put the dishes to soak, maybe have herself another helping of the delicious crème caramel Eleanor had made for dessert, and then do a few dozen laps in the pool before she went to bed. She had taken, lately, to doing her laps at night instead of in the morning. It helped her sleep.

Sometimes.

Other times—most times—she ended up reading until she finally dropped off. Scripts, mostly, in hopes of finding a screenplay where the woman wasn't cast as the victim or used as mere set decoration. She'd discovered the scripts made a good soporific, far superior to either liquor or pills and without the unpleasant side effects.

She heard the soft clatter of cutlery against china as she approached the door to the dining room and quickened her steps, the silk faille of her wide-legged evening pajamas swishing against her legs with the quick movement, the heels of her shoes clicking sharply against the hardwood floor.

There was one more hurdle to be faced before she could be alone with her thoughts and the night. One more obstacle to be overcome and conquered. Squaring her shoulders for the battle ahead, she lifted her chin and stepped into the dining room. "Just what do you think you're doing?" she demanded of her ex-husband.

6

ZEKE LOOKED UP at his ex-wife and then down at the precariously balanced stack of cups and saucers he was holding as if the answer should be obvious. "Clearing the table."

"I can see that," Ariel said, her voice tight with exhaustion and controlled fury. "Why?"

"Well..." He shrugged innocently, as if he had no idea why she was upset. "I heard you tell Eleanor you wouldn't need her anymore tonight after she served dessert, so I thought I'd give you a hand with the cleaning up. It seemed the least I could do since you hosted the dinner."

"I don't need help with the cleaning up," Ariel informed him. "Because I'm not going to clean up. Eleanor will take care of it in the morning. So you can go," she added, with the frosty hauteur of a queen.

"You never used to be so unfeeling," Zeke chided, reaching out to pinch three brandy snifters between his fingers before he headed for the kitchen.

Ariel followed him as far as the door. "Unfeeling?" she said to his back, watching as he set the glasses and china on the ceramic tile counter next to the stainless steel sink. "What do you mean by that?"

"Eleanor is—what?—nearly sixty years old? I'd think you'd be a little more considerate of her, is all."

Ariel closed her eyes and counted to ten. Slowly.

"Excuse me," Zeke murmured, an edge of humor in his deep voice.

Ariel opened her eyes and found herself staring at the soft hollow at the base of his throat, revealed by the open collar of his soft tobacco brown silk shirt. She stepped back hastily, as if touching him would contaminate her, and let him pass back into the dining room.

"I don't know why you decided to stay behind when everyone else has had the good manners to go home," she said as he moved around the table gathering up the dessert plates and cutlery. "And I don't particularly care. I— Will you please put that down and listen to me?" she snapped, grabbing the cut crystal brandy decanter out of his hand. She slammed it down onto the table without regard for its cost or fragility, and then reached for the gold-rimmed dessert plates in his other hand and slammed them down, too. The sterling silver dessert spoons he'd placed on top of the stack of delicate china plates clattered to the table. "I want you out of here, Zeke," she said with quiet desperation. "Now."

Zeke shook his head. "We need to talk."

"You and I have nothing to say to each other."

"We have a daughter," he said calmly, "who's planning a wedding. I'd say that gives us plenty to talk about."

"That's what the meetings with the wedding consultants are for," Ariel countered. "To talk about the wedding. And since that's already been planned and discussed to the nth degree, I don't see that there's anything at all left to talk about."

"Ariel." He reached out as if to touch her.

She stepped back, out of reach.

He sighed and ran his hand through his hair instead. "Isn't it time we called a truce?"

"I thought we had."

Zeke shook his head. "This is just a temporary cease-fire until the wedding's over. I'm talking about a real truce. Because the wedding isn't going to be the end of it, you know. In three or four years there'll be grand-children. Christenings. Birthdays. Christmas. Cameron isn't going to want to divide their lives between us the way we did hers. And we have no right to ask it of her."

Ariel stared at him for a long moment, knowing he was right but not wanting him to be. "I know," she said, finally. "I've thought about that, too."

"Then do we have a truce?"

Ariel sighed, and then nodded. "I guess it's time we tried to make some sort of real peace," she agreed. "For Cameron's sake."

"You might start by looking at me," Zeke suggested, "instead of staring off over my left shoulder some-where."

"I look at you."

"No," Zeke said. "You don't." He reached out and grasped her chin, turning her face up to his. "This is looking at me," he said, when she finally lifted her gaze to his.

They stared at each other for a long five seconds, glaring at each other, really, each trying to overpower the other and prevail through sheer force of personality.

She's still got the deepest, bluest, most fathomless eyes in the world, he was thinking. *And the sweetest, most kissable mouth known to man. And the softest skin imaginable.*

He'd always loved the way her skin felt under his fingertips, like warm living silk that responded to his slightest touch. As if, he thought, she were fashioned to respond to him, and only him.

He hasn't changed, Ariel thought. *He still has a gaze that would melt the polar ice cap. And a mouth made to drive a woman crazy. And hard, gentle hands.*

She'd always loved the way his hands felt on her skin, his fingers as delicate and gentle as if he were stroking a baby, as knowing as if he'd programmed her every erotic response. Which in a way, she thought, he had.

She swayed toward him, slightly. And he bent his head, slightly. And then they both gasped and jerked away as if they'd gotten too close to a flame.

"All right. We'll call a truce," Ariel said, hastily backing away from him. She smoothed her hands down the front of her peach silk tunic, touching the satin frogs as if to make sure they were still securely fastened. "Grab that bottle—" she nodded at the crystal decanter "—and a couple of clean snifters off the sideboard in the living room. I'll take the rest of these things into the kitchen and put them to soak. We'll meet out by the pool in five minutes and hammer out the conditions of the truce."

And then she turned, grabbing up the plates and the cutlery she had slammed down a moment ago, and fled to the safety of the kitchen without pausing to see if he was following her instructions.

She was no more immune to him now than she had ever been, she realized as she stood at the sink running hot water over the dishes. He still had the power to move her in ways that no one else ever had. Raw animal lust, her mother had called it when Ariel had first fallen for him all those years ago. And maybe she had

been right. Maybe it *was* simple chemistry. Just the basic biological pull of woman to man. Pure unadulterated sex. But it felt neither simple, nor basic, nor pure.

Instead, the feeling was rich and complex, full of nu-
ance and subtlety. It was as hot and sweet as young
love, as wickedly provocative as an illicit affair. It was
vital and alive and powerful. And dangerous. Very,
very dangerous.

Because Zeke's masculine appeal spread out like an
interstate, in a dozen different directions, toward a
dozen different women. Almost any woman, as far as
she could tell. They were all drawn to his powerful life
force, to the blatant sex appeal and charm he radiated
like the sun radiated warmth. And, like the sun, he
happily, generously, bestowed his abundant charm on
any flower who turned her face to him. He always
had....

"THANKS, BABE," Zeke said and delivered a smacking
kiss to the hand of the young female hairdresser who'd
just finished blow-drying his hair into carefully artless
disarray around the red bandanna he wore as a headband. "You can run your talented little fingers through
my hair any time."

The hairdresser giggled and jerked her hand away,
reaching out as if to slap him on the arm. The playful
blow looked more like a caress from where Ariel was
sitting, having her own hair redone for the next scene.
The woman's fingers seemed to linger on Zeke's biceps
for a moment, and then he yelped and reached out,
grabbing her around the waist and tumbling her into
his lap.

"Pinch me, will you?" Ariel heard him say, just before he bent his head to the hairdresser's neck. The

woman shrieked, squirming around in his lap without, Ariel thought, really trying to get away. And then
the tall director's chair tilted, listing backward, and
with a laugh Zeke leaned forward and set her on her
feet. "That'll teach you to mess with a star," he said,
reaching out to smack her on her fanny as she sashayed away.

She turned and cheerfully gave him the finger.

Zeke laughed again and turned to look at Ariel.

She quickly averted her eyes, shifting her gaze from
Zeke's mirrored image to that of the hairdresser standing behind her, brushing out her long blond hair.

"You 'bout ready there?" Zeke asked her as he pro-
pelled himself out of the high, canvas-backed chair. "It
looks like Hans is about set up for us." He put his hand
on Ariel's shoulder as he spoke and gave it a little
squeeze. She stiffened, just slightly, but enough to let
him know his caress wasn't welcome. Zeke lifted his
hand and looked down at her. "What's the matter,
sweetheart?"

She shook her head and glanced significantly at her
hairdresser.

"Would you excuse us for a minute, please, Mar-
sha?" Zeke said politely, waiting until the hairdresser
had moved away. Then he swung around in front of
Ariel's chair and leaned in, a hand balanced on either
wooden arm. "Okay, sweetheart, give. What's the
matter?"

"Really, Zeke," Ariel said primly. "This isn't very
discreet. I thought we agreed that we'd keep our..." She
hesitated slightly, still a little uncomfortable with the
new intimacy between them and not sure of what to call
it " . . . our relationship a secret."

"No, *we* didn't agree," Zeke reminded her. "You insisted and I went along with it. For now," he added warningly. "And, just so you know," he said, leaning forward until they were almost nose-to-nose, "I don't intend to put up with this secrecy for very much longer. I want the whole world to know about us and how we feel about each other."

Ariel couldn't help it, her gaze slid sideways to where the two hairdressers stood talking. "And how do we feel about each other?"

"Oh, so *that's* what this is all about," he murmured knowingly, following her glance. "You're not giving me the cold shoulder because you're worried about somebody reporting back to your mother about us. You're jealous," he crowed, obviously delighted with the discovery.

"I am not jealous."

"Yes, you are," he countered gleefully. "You're practically turning green with it." And then, when she didn't respond to his lighthearted cajolery, he reached between them and lifted her chin with the tip of his finger. "There's nothing for you to be jealous of, sweetheart, don't you know that? I was only teasing her. The same way I tease all the ladies."

And it was true, she knew, he teased every female on the set from the fifty-two-year old wardrobe mistress to the nine-year-old actress playing Laura Simmons's younger sister. And they all teased him back, charmed and delighted to be the object of his attentions.

"It's just the way I am," he said, his dark eyes sincere and serious. "I like the ladies and the ladies like me. But it doesn't mean anything. Honest."

AND HE WAS RIGHT, Ariel thought as she stood there at the sink, watching soap bubbles billow up around the dirty dishes. It *was* just the way he was. And it *didn't* mean anything. Not to him, anyway.

But it meant a lot to her and, she suspected, to any number of other women who'd been foolish enough to give him their hearts over the years. It wasn't that he broke them deliberately. She realized that now, although she hadn't twenty-five years ago. Zeke wasn't cruel; he was just . . . careless. Not, Ariel admitted to herself—rather magnanimously, she thought—that the blame for the trail of broken hearts behind him could be laid *entirely* at Zeke's door. He was so effortlessly charming and so blatantly, unabashedly male that women gave their hearts to him whether he asked for them or not. It wasn't his fault if they followed him around like willing, wiggling puppies with their tongues hanging out, begging for the tiniest scrap of his attention and affection.

He *could* be blamed, however, for the easy, heedless way he accepted what they offered without, apparently, sparing a single thought for the consequences. She certainly blamed him for the careless way he'd accepted her naive offerings of love—and then turned right around and stepped into bed with another woman on that awful night at the Bachelor Arms.

Well, she wouldn't make that mistake again. So, okay, she wasn't immune to him—not by a long shot, she thought with a shiver—but she was a levelheaded, clear-sighted adult now, not a wide-eyed woman-child with a head full of dreams.

She turned off the water with a hard twist, wiped her hands on a kitchen towel and let herself out the back door of the kitchen, onto the smooth quarry stone tile of the patio surrounding the pool. The pool lights were on, wavering seductively under the surface of the water. The night air was soft and warm, perfumed with the scent of the orange and lemon trees planted in tubs strategically placed around the perimeter of the patio.

Zeke was there, waiting for her, sitting at one of the wicker and glass tables. He'd taken off his oatmeal linen sport coat and rolled the sleeves of his soft brown silk shirt halfway up his hair-dusted forearms. His right ankle was propped negligently atop his left knee. His brandy glass was balanced against the inside of his powerful thigh. His thick, sable hair, always too long, curled over the tops of his ears and down the back of his neck to touch the collar of his shirt. There was silver in the temples now, just a touch, and the very fact that he hadn't felt the need to color it only added to his rugged masculinity. Something about the way he was sitting there reminded her, suddenly, of the way he had perched atop that big black Harley-Davidson all those years ago. Cocky, self-assured, aware of his almost irresistible appeal to the opposite sex.

Ariel took a deep breath and reminded herself that, although she might not be immune to his charm, she'd been vaccinated. And one dose of heartache, administered by Zeke Blackstone, was more than enough.

He rose as she approached him, instinctively polite, and she waved him back down, reaching to pull out her own chair before he could put his brandy down and do it for her. It scraped across the stone tiles and then the old wicker creaked comfortably as she sat down. Zeke sat back down too and reached out with his free hand, pushing the crystal snifter he'd filled for her across the table.

"Did I tell you how absolutely stunning you look tonight?" he said as she picked it up.

Ariel tried, very hard, to control the spurt of pleasure that zinged through her at his words. She'd taken special pains with her appearance this evening. Because it was a special occasion, she told herself. But also because she was just vindictive enough to hope Zeke might feel some regret for what he'd so carelessly thrown away all those years ago. "It isn't necessary to flatter me," she said dismissively, and lifted the snifter to her lips for a small sip.

"It's not flattery when it's the truth," Zeke said. "You're an exquisitely beautiful woman. You always have been." He lifted his glass to her in a silent toast and then brought it to his nose, swirling the contents to release more of the heady fumes, and took a deep drink.

The expression in his eyes when he lowered the glass and looked at her was wry and self-deprecating. "Before we get started on the peace negotiations, I want to apologize."

"Apologize?" Ariel said, startled. After all these years he wanted to apologize? Now?

"For that little performance at dinner. It was in poor taste, especially with my own daughter sitting there."

Ariel took a careful sip of her own drink to hide her disappointment. "Yes," she said, when she lowered the glass. "It was."

"But you made me so damned mad," Zeke continued, excusing himself with his very next breath. "Pretending what we had back then was nothing."

"In the overall scheme of things, it *was* nothing."

"It gave us Cameron."

"You're right," she agreed after a moment. "And I'm sorry, too," she said simply. "I shouldn't have tried to make it seem less than it was. It wasn't fair to Cameron to make it sound as if she'd been conceived in anything but love."

They looked at each other for a long moment, hovering on the edge of . . . something. Some earth-shattering discovery. Some startling admission. Something.

"It was love, wasn't it?" Zeke said softly, his dark eyes warm and compelling at he stared at her across the table.

Ariel looked down into her glass, fighting back sudden, inexplicable tears. "I thought so at the time," she whispered.

Zeke sighed. "So did I," he said with quiet fervor. "Dammit, so did I."

He threw back the last of his brandy with a quick, savage gesture, then set the empty snifter down on the table with a sharp click. Ariel looked at him, a little startled, waiting for what he would do next. He stretched his hand out across the table, palm up.

"For the sake of our daughter and the love we once had," he said. "Truce?"

Ariel hesitated for a moment. Uncertain. Wary. And then she set her brandy snifter down and put her hand in his. "Truce," she whispered.

They sat there in the soft night air for a moment, silent, their hands tightly clasped, staring at each other across the width of the patio table. It was almost as if they were seeing each other for the first time. And, yet, not at all like the first time.

She was no longer the wide-eyed innocent.

He was no longer the cocky young stud.

They were adults now, their youthful passion tempered by experience and heartache. And, yet, the attraction was still there, as strong—maybe stronger—than ever. They both felt it, like a jolt of electricity, running from one to the other and back again, generating a deep, wild, fast-burning fire. They both saw it, glowing, beckoning like twin beacons in two pairs of eyes. Deep, fathomless blue. Hot smoldering brown. Both full of unspoken, soul-deep yearning, unrelenting needs and a desire that hadn't dimmed in twenty-five years.

Ariel was the first to take flight, stirring restlessly, trying to slip her hand out of his. Zeke's fingers tightened.

"Ariel," he murmured achingly, his deep voice softer, more seductive, than the night air.

"No," she said, but the word was little more than a movement of her lips and her fingers lay acquiescent in his.

"Ariel." He rose on the word, drawing her up with him by the hand he still held.

"Oh, no," she murmured, but she responded like a marionette to the puppeteer's strings, allowing him to draw her around the table.

"Oh, God, *Ariel*," he groaned and gently enfolded her in his arms.

She went to him, pliant and unresisting, melting against the hardness of his chest, mindlessly seeking the heat that had always matched her own burning desire. He held her tightly for a moment, crushing her to him, relishing the feel of her small, soft breasts against his chest, cherishing the delicacy of her slender body beneath the fragile silk that covered it. She held him just as tightly, her arms wrapped around his lean waist, her hands flat against his broad back, savoring the inexplicable, inexpressible deliciousness of his hard, male body pressed tight against the softness of hers.

There was no thought of the past between them just then. No memories. No regrets. No what-ifs or might-have-beens or if-onlys. There was just here and now. Need and desire and intemperate, unrestrained, overwhelming heat.

He slid his hands up to her head, tilting it back for his kiss, but she had already lifted her chin, offering her lips before he could take them. They tasted each other with avid, open mouths, using lips and tongues and teeth in an orgy of nibbling and licking, nipping and plunging. They were greedy, both of them, their heads turning, their lips parting, realigning, then coming together as they sought just the right pressure and position. The pair of delicate cloisonne combs holding Ariel's hair in its fashionable twist fell, unheeded, to the stone tiles as Zeke's hands moved in her hair. The back of Zeke's shirt was crushed in her clutching fingers as she tried to pull him closer. They found the right angle, suddenly, and their mouths melded, grinding against each other, moist, eager, open, hot.

Ariel whimpered and pressed closer, lifting herself up on tiptoe to deepen the pressure of his mouth on hers.

Zeke groaned and slid his hands down her back, cupping them over her buttocks to lift her to his body.

Ariel stiffened in sudden alarm as he ground his erection into her lower belly. Panicked, she tore her mouth away from his.

"Zeke. Zeke, sto—"

He shifted one hand to the back of her head to hold her still for more of his kisses.

She let go of his shirt, slid her hands around to his chest and pushed. Hard. It was pushing against a stone wall. She squirmed against him, trying to wriggle out of his grasp, but he only groaned in appreciation and flexed his fingers against the soft globes in his hands. In desperation, she went limp.

It took a moment or two, but Zeke stilled and lifted his head. "Ariel?"

"Let go of me, Zeke. Please."

He slid his hands up to the small of her back, loosening his hold just enough so that he could see her face. "What is it?" he asked, but he was pretty sure he knew.

She was having second thoughts, when he would have preferred that she not think at all. Thinking would only cloud the issue. Women, he thought sourly—his own higher functions clouded with an excess of testosterone and emotion—did far too much thinking at times like this.

"This shouldn't have happened," she said, confirming his worst suspicions.

"But it did," he said, with irrefutable male logic.

"It shouldn't have," she repeated, more vehemently. "And we both know it. It's wrong and it's stupid."

He smiled and tried to cuddle her closer, instinctively resorting to charm and cajolery to win her over. "It doesn't feel wrong," he murmured, neatly avoiding the question of stupidity.

"I'm sure very little feels wrong to you when it comes to sex." Her tone was icicle cool and scathing, her body suddenly stiff in a way it hadn't been before. "Others of us have more discriminating standards. Now, let me go."

Stung by her coldness, he did as she asked. "You never used to be so cold," he said, his voice flat with the hurt she had inflicted.

"I never used to be a lot of things." She crossed her arms over the front of her body, rubbing her palms against the sleeves of her silk tunic as if she were cold. The look in her blue eyes was hot enough to melt steel. "But that was before I found the man who professed to love me in bed with another woman."

7

ARIEL STOOD BY the window in her darkened bedroom, breathless, hot, shaking, her gaze fastened on Zeke as he stood staring into the depths of her swimming pool. He hadn't followed her when she'd turned and walked into the house, as she'd half expected, half *hoped* he would do. He hadn't reached out to try and stop her. He hadn't, in fact, said another word after she'd thrown her accusation at him.

Just like the last time.

He didn't deny it.

He didn't try to explain.

He didn't apologize.

He'd just looked...pained, she thought, as if she had unfairly accused him of some heinous crime. If she hadn't seen the evidence with her own eyes, hadn't caught him in the act of betrayal herself, she might actually believe his look of wounded innocence.

But she had caught him. Red-handed. *En flagrant délit.* Well, she amended mentally, not actually *in* the act. Thank God. But as close to it as to make no difference in a court of law—or a woman's heart. She'd seen all she needed to see that awful night to know her mother had been right about Zeke all along. Even if she'd been proven wrong about a number of other things, she'd known Zeke was trouble from the first.

Where women were concerned, he couldn't be trusted. And she couldn't live with a man she couldn't trust. No matter how much she might have loved him. She didn't have it in her to play the blind, complacent wife, then or—

Her heart leapt into her throat as Zeke suddenly gave up staring into the pool and turned his head to look up at her bedroom windows. He stood there for a long moment, his gaze fixed, and she felt as if he could see her standing behind the white satin swags decorating the tall glass doors, staring at him. Ariel held her breath, waiting ... waiting ... but his broad shoulders merely lifted in a sigh and he ran his hand through his hair and turned away, disappearing into the darkness beyond the lights of the pool. He'd left. Again. Without trying to see her or explain. A crushing sense of disappointment washed over Ariel as she stood there at the window and watched him walk away.

She wasn't immune, after all, she realized. She hadn't even built up any resistance in the last twenty-five years. One look, one touch, one kiss, and she was right back where she'd started. A one-man woman, hopelessly, helplessly, irrevocably in love with a man who would never be satisfied with just one woman. It was a surefire recipe for heartache and disaster.

And she had known it, instinctively, even back when she was a naive and lovesick eighteen-year-old. Or why else would she have hesitated to accept his ring?

SHE COULD TELL Zeke was excited and wound up when he picked her up for their date that evening. And who wouldn't be? They'd shot the final scene of *Wild Hearts* early that morning and Hans Ostfield and the film editor were already closeted away in some office on the studio lot, cutting and splicing the raw, out-of-sequence footage into a polished work of art. At least, that's what

Hans had said it would be when he and the editor were finished with it, and no one had any reason to doubt him. The dailies had been great throughout the shooting and there was a pleasant buzz of excitement working its way through the small-town community that was Hollywood. People in the know were expecting *Wild Hearts* to make money and careers.

And one of those careers was going to be Zeke Blackstone's.

In celebration of that fact, Zeke had borrowed Eric Shannon's beat-up old '66 van with its psychedelic paint job and a thin old camping mattress in the back. He'd also bought a picnic supper of thick sandwiches, potato salad and fat kosher dill pickles from a local deli.

"It's not real deli. Not like you'd get in New York," he told Ariel as he finished spreading the picnic out on the sleeping bag he'd opened up in the back of the van. There were paper napkins and plastic forks, and two small flickering white candles in blue votive holders. "It's not bad though. And we've got this to wash it down." He grinned at her and pulled a large green bottle out of the ice chest as if he were pulling a rabbit out of a hat. "Dom Pérignon. The guy at the liquor store said it was the best champagne money can buy."

Ariel's stomach lurched a bit at the thought of alcohol but she couldn't help but smile at his enthusiasm. He did everything with such passion and verve, such gung ho style. She sat quietly, as always, her legs neatly folded to the side, and watched him deal with the foil wrapping and wire harness on the top of the bottle.

"There's supposed to be some kind of trick to opening one of these so it hardly makes any noise at all and you end up looking as cool as James Bond." He curled his long fingers around the neck of the bottle, pressed his thumbs against the cork and aimed it out the wide open back doors of the van. "But I don't know what it is, so you'd better get the glasses out of that grocery bag there—" he nodded his head at the bag in question "—and be ready."

The cork refused to budge for a moment, then came loose with a resounding pop and arced out into the night. Champagne frothed up out of the top of the bottle and over Zeke's hands. "The glasses. Quick," he instructed, when Ariel just sat there, staring at the single deep pink rose surrounded by baby's breath and wrapped in cellophane that had been in the bag with the glasses. *He bought me a rose.* "Ariel, the glasses."

"Oh, sorry." She put the rose down, yanked the champagne glasses out of the bag and held them out, leaning far enough out of the back door of the van so that none of the cold sticky liquid would drip on her white bell-bottom hip-huggers or the sleeping bag.

Zeke filled the glasses slowly, carefully, making sure there was more liquid than bubbles in them, then set the bottle aside and took one of the brimming glasses from Ariel. Holding it aloft, he grinned at her over the rim. "A toast," he said, waiting for her to lift her glass, as well.

She smiled and echoed his gesture.

"To Hollywood," he said grandly, and drained half the glass in one gulp.

Ariel just sat there, her glass raised, staring at him. *To Hollywood?* He'd brought her up here in a van with a sleeping bag and a mattress in the back, to park on a secluded road in the foothills of the Santa Monica Mountains overlooking L.A., with candles and champagne and a pink rose and he wanted to toast Hollywood?

Was her mother right, after all? Was his career really more important to him than she was?

"I'm going to own this town someday," he said, his gaze directed out over the view, drinking in the vista of twinkling lights and the fifty-foot-high letters of the Hollywood sign on Mt. Cahuenga. "Or a good part of it, anyway. *Wild Hearts* is just the beginning for me. I've been offered two other movie roles already, just on the strength of the buzz, and my agent says there'll be dozens more after *Wild Hearts* comes out. She says I'll be able to write my own ticket. Do just about anything I want. I've already told her I want to direct, too, eventually. And produce. Hell, I might even have my own production company some day."

"That sounds very...ambitious," Ariel said hesitantly, wondering where she fit in to his grand scheme.

"It's what I've always wanted. Ever since I was a little kid, growing up in a fifth floor walk-up in the Bronx, all I ever wanted was to be one of those guys up there on the movie screen. Well—" he grinned at her "—after I got over wanting to be a fireman, that is." The grin faded when she didn't respond. "You're not drinking the champagne. Don't you like it?"

"No, it's fine," Ariel said, and took a sip.

Zeke gave an exaggerated sigh. "Not even ol' Dom Pérignon is going to turn you into a drinker, is he? Well, that's okay," he said indulgently. "I got a six-pack of Coke, too." He tossed off the rest of his champagne, put the glass down and twisted around, reaching into the ice chest for a bottle of Coke. After drying it off on the hem of his black T-shirt, he removed the top and handed it to her, reaching out to take her still full champagne glass with his other hand. "It's your turn to make a toast," he said.

"With Coke?"

"Sure." He shrugged negligently. "It's wet and bubbly, isn't it? Go on." He lifted his glass. "Make a toast."

Ariel hesitated for a moment, unsure of what to make a toast to. Hollywood was just a town to her, not a place to be conquered and owned. And success was something that had happened at an age when she didn't even know what it was. As for ambition, it was something other people had for her; she'd never had any of it herself. Until lately. But was love a true ambition? Was marriage?

"To *Wild Hearts*," she said at last because it was something they had in common. Maybe the only thing they had in common, if her mother turned out to be right, after all.

"A woman after my own heart," Zeke said approvingly and leaned over the flickering candles to kiss her. He put his champagne glass down on top of the ice chest. "You want turkey or pastrami?"

She chose turkey, and then nibbled on it halfheartedly as he wolfed down the other sandwich and filled her in on his life's dreams between bites.

"I want a beach house in Malibu," he said. "And a brownstone in Greenwich Village for Ma and the girls. I'd move them out to live with me in California but they'd never come. Well . . ." He thought about it a minute as he chewed a mouthful of pastrami and rye bread. "Maybe Ruthie would, when she finishes high school. But Ma and Sarah June are died-in-the-wool New Yorkers." He flashed her a grin. "They both think civilization stops at the Hudson River. Ma thinks California is full of hippies and drug addicts."

Ariel smiled and nodded, and wondered again where she fitted into his grandiose plans. In all his ramblings about his future, he hadn't mentioned her place in it even once.

Was the love affair over now that they'd finished filming *Wild Hearts*? Had he only been romancing her to further his career, just as her mother had said? Had he only been making sure that the love scenes rang true by making love to her offscreen as well as on? Was that why he'd given in so easily when she'd insisted they keep their relationship secret?

It wasn't secret, of course. Everyone on the set knew they were seeing each other. The studio bosses knew; the TV execs from *Family Fortune* knew; her mother knew. Even the teen movie magazines were hinting that "television's sweet little Chrissy Fortune" might finally, actually have a real boyfriend. But no one, she thought, knew their relationship had become so intimate. Not for sure—although her mother had been very vocal with her suspicions.

"What's the matter, sweetheart?" Zeke asked, breaking into her thoughts. "You're not eating. Isn't the sandwich any good? Would you like some of my pastrami?"

Ariel put her sandwich down, giving up even the pretense of eating. It wasn't sitting very well in her stomach, anyway. "I'm just not hungry, I guess."

"Are you upset about something?" He leaned forward, peering into her face over the candlelight. "Has your mother been on your case again about seeing me?"

"Not any more than usual."

"Then what is it?"

"It's nothing, really. I just feel . . ." She shrugged. "I don't know. Sad, somehow." And uncertain. So desperately uncertain of where she stood with him.

Zeke nodded as if he understood perfectly. "It's the letdown because the filming is over. I feel it, too, a little," he consoled her. "It's probably a pretty normal reaction. But I have a surefire cure." He gave her a sweet, sexy leer and began gathering up the remains of their picnic supper. "You just trust yourself to ol' Dr. Blackstone," he said, wriggling his eyebrows at her as he moved the candles to the top of the ice chest where they'd be out of harm's way, "and I'll have you feeling more cheerful in no time." He reached out and grasped her by the shoulders, tumbling her onto her back on the sleeping bag.

But, for once, the sight of Zeke leaning over her, his eyes all dark and smoldering and hungry, failed to ignite an answering spark in her.

"Hey, you really are blue, aren't you?" He let go of her and rolled over onto his back. Stretching out to his full length on the floor of the van, he dug one hand into the tight front pocket of his jeans. "Here." He sat up and picked her hand up in his. "Maybe this will cheer you up," he said, pressing something into her palm.

It was a small velvet-covered box. Ariel's heart began to pound. She sat up and very carefully, very slowly, held her hands so that the flickering light of the candles shone on the box as she opened it. It was a ring, a small but exquisite sapphire, surrounded by tiny diamonds. She looked up, her gaze shifting from the ring to his face and back again. Did he mean it to be an engagement ring? Or something else entirely?

"I know it's not much," he said defensively, obviously misinterpreting her unbelieving gaze. "But it's all

I can afford right now. We can exchange it for a bigger one later if you—"

Ariel licked her lips. "Are you *proposing* to me?" she asked carefully.

Zeke gave her an exasperated look. "What the hell else do you think I'd be doing, giving you a ring? Of course, I'm proposing to you." He took the box away from her and plucked the ring out, holding it in two fingers. "Do you want it or not?"

"Oh, Zeke."

"Is that a yes?"

"Oh, Zeke."

"I'll take that as a yes," he decided and slipped the ring onto her finger.

"Oh, *Zeke*," she said again, and threw herself into his arms, nearly knocking him over.

He pushed her back down onto the sleeping bag and proceeded to kiss her senseless.

She ignited instantly this time, bursting into full flame in a matter of seconds. "Make love to me," she demanded, yanking open the metal buttons on his jeans. "Make love to me right now."

It was the first sexually aggressive move she'd ever made toward him and Zeke responded to it the way any healthy, red-blooded, twenty-two-year-old male might be expected to respond. He reached for the zipper on her little white bell-bottoms, pulled it down and peeled her out of her pants so fast it was a wonder she didn't get fabric burns on her thighs. As he reached for the hem of her baby blue poorboy sweater, intending to drag it off over her head, she slipped her hand inside his jeans and gently squeezed him.

Zeke nearly hit the ceiling of the van. "Good God Almighty," he breathed. "*Ariel*."

"Now, Zeke," she demanded breathlessly. "Right now."

He let go of the sweater and rushed to obey her, pushing his jeans and underpants down just far enough to let his erection spring free. She opened her thighs as he lifted himself over her, shamelessly exposing the urgency of her need. He plunged himself in to the hilt, entering her without caution or restriction. Her hips rolled against his convulsively, pleading and demanding at the same time. He thrust deeply, and then thrust again, and the ride to completion began. It was wild. Unrestrained. Hot. And very, very brief. Ariel climaxed with a fierce, sharp cry of feminine triumph and Zeke followed her barely a second later, his shout of satisfaction coming so close upon hers that it sounded as if they came from a single throat.

The recovery took longer than the act itself. They lay, still joined together, listening to each other breathe as they struggled to come back to reality.

"I guess I should propose more often," Zeke said and she could hear the humor and pleasure in his deep voice.

"I don't know what came over me," she whispered, a bit embarrassed now that the urgency was past.

"Whatever it was, I hope it happens again. And again." Zeke lifted his head and kissed her. "And again. It'll probably kill me, but I'll die happy." He rolled off her, turning onto his back, and pulled her on top of him. "Damn, we're going to make a great team!" he said, smiling up into her face. "We'll take this town by storm."

"Team?"

"Like Bogie and Bacall, Tracy and Hepburn, Gable and Lombard. The names Blackstone and Cameron on a marquee will sell tickets by the millions. We'll have our pick of all the best scripts, the best directors, the best everything."

Ariel pushed herself up onto her hands to look down at him. "You want us to act together again?" she said carefully.

"You heard what Hans said. We're going be box-office magic."

Ariel wriggled off him and sat up, folding her legs under her so that she was perched on her knees beside him. Was that what his marriage proposal was all about? A ploy to make sure they'd be working to-gether again? She hated herself for even thinking it but . . .

"I can only make movies when *Family Fortune* is on summer hiatus," she said, to test him. "And the net-work execs have some say on what roles I can take."

"Your contract is up at the end of this season," he re-minded her, "so the network bigwigs won't have any say for much longer."

"Unless we renew. My mother's in the middle of ne-gotiations with them right now. She's my agent, you know."

"She doesn't have to be," he said easily. "I'm sure my agent would be more than happy to represent you."

"My mother's managed my career since I shot my first breakfast cereal commercial when I was four years old," Ariel said, looking down at her engagement ring as she spoke. Her mood was now pensive and al-most . . . regretful. It was such a beautiful ring. "And she's done a great job."

"Up until now, sure," Zeke countered, reaching up to tuck a trailing lock of blond hair behind her ear. "But

I don't think she understands that you're beyond breakfast food commercials and silly sitcoms now."

Ariel went very still. "That silly sitcom has been one of the top-ten rated shows on TV for the last seven years."

"Granted. But it's not going to go two more. You know that, sweetheart," he said cajolingly. "You've said so yourself."

"Maybe so." Ariel reached around behind her for her panties and bell-bottoms as she spoke and drew them onto her lap, half-consciously seeking to cover and protect herself. "But I owe everyone on the show those two years. I owe my mother those two years, too."

There was a long moment of charged silence. "And what about what you owe me?"

"And what do I owe you?"

"I'm the man you just agreed to marry, for heaven's sake!" He yanked his jeans up and jackknifed to a sitting position. "I'd think the answer to that would be obvious."

"I guess I'm a little thick." Ariel pressed her lips together and willed herself not to cry. "You're going to have to be more specific."

"I'd say you owe me at least the same consideration you owe your mother and the people you work with."

"And what about what you owe me?" she asked quietly. "What about understanding my point of view? And my career goals?" *What about love?* she wanted to ask, realizing, at that moment, that he hadn't said the word at any time during his proposal to her. He hadn't said the word at all, not since the very first time they'd made love. She held her breath, waiting for him . . . willing him . . . to say it now.

"Oh, hell, Ariel, this is ridiculous. We shouldn't be talking about owing each other anything." He reached out and grasped her shoulders in his hands. "Two people in love aren't supposed to think about what they owe each other. That isn't the way it works."

There, she told herself, *he said the word.*

So why didn't she believe it?

"I do love you, sweetheart," he said, as if he sensed her disbelief. "You must know that. I guess the question is, do you love me?"

"You know I do," she whispered achingly, "but . . ."

His hands tightened on her shoulders. "But what?"

"I don't th..." She took a deep breath and tried again. "I don't think we should be engaged right now. Not..not formally," she said, hurrying through it as the thunderclouds formed on his face. "We can be engaged secretly but—"

"Secretly," he spat out, and pushed her away from him.

She fell backward, onto her hands. She used the motion to shift her legs around to the front so she could pull her pants on.

"I've had just about all the so-called secrecy I can stomach," he hissed. "Hell, it's not as if your mother doesn't already know about us. Or anyone who was on the set of *Wild Hearts*, for that matter. Our relationship stopped being a secret about two days after it started."

"But nobody knows the whole truth about us," she said as she yanked up the zipper on her bell-bottoms. "Nobody knows we're—"

"—sleeping together, is that it? Nobody knows and you don't want anybody to know, do you? Are you that ashamed of the fact that American's sweetheart is actually having sex? Or is it me? Are you ashamed of me, Ariel?"

"No. No, I'm not ashamed." But she was, in a way. Not of Zeke, but of the fact that she was having sex at all. And unsanctified sex, at that. It might have been the era of women's liberation and sexual freedom but Ariel was scarcely a child of her times. She'd been under her mother's thumb for too long, protected from the turmoil and change of the sixties in the unreal worlds of Beverly Hills and a studio sound stage.

Add to that her doubts about Zeke's true feelings for her and his ability to be faithful—doubts that were actively encouraged by her mother—and was it any wonder she was confused and uncertain?

"It's just that I . . . that I have an image to protect, that's all," she said finally, falling back on the line her mother had been spoon-feeding her since she was old enough to understand what the phrase meant.

"An image to protect!"

"It would just be until the new contracts were signed," she said, trying to placate him. "Once they're signed, it won't matter and we can announce our engagement."

"It won't matter—" he began furiously, and then stopped.

Ariel waited, watching him pull himself together. It took several long moments, several deep breaths, while he sat there with his hands on his thighs, his eyes closed. When he opened them again, they were clear and direct—and furious.

"I was hoping we could announce our engagement at the wrap party on Friday night," he said in a deceptively calm voice. "But if we can't—" he shrugged "—well, then, I'd rather not announce it at all. Ever."

8

ZEKE PACED up and down the small living room of apartment 1-G, furious with himself, furious with Ariel. Just plain furious, period.

She'd done it to him again. Put him in the wrong again, made him feel guilty over something that had never happened in the first place.

He hadn't had sex with that woman. Hell, he'd been in no condition that night to have sex with anyone, even if Ariel herself had slipped naked and willing into bed beside him....

"JEEZ, BLACKSTONE, if you plan to hang around here all night looking like that, you're gonna ruin the party."

"What party is that?" Zeke asked as he stood, barefoot and unshaven, in front of the refrigerator, trying to decide whether a six-pack of beer or one of the half gallon jugs of Gallo rosé would send him to oblivion more quickly. He thought a pint of hard liquor would accomplish the task in less time than either the beer or the wine, but they didn't have any in the apartment and he didn't feel like going out and getting it.

"It's sort of a double celebration," Eric Shannon informed him. "Ethan's gig on *As Time Goes By* is permanent as of this morning—the dashing and debonair Dr. Brick Merriweather is officially on staff at daytime TV's Meadowland General. And Alan Boyd has made a firm offer on *Lovers And Strangers*," he said, referring to the screenplay he and his younger brother Jack had been working on for the last six months. "As soon as we sign on the dotted line, Jack and I are outta here and headed for easy street."

"No kidding?" Zeke said, trying to inject some enthusiasm into his voice over his roommates' good luck. "That's great."

"Yeah," Eric said. "Try not to get too excited."

"No, really, man, I mean it," Zeke said. "That's great news. I'm happy for you guys."

"Happy for who?" Ethan asked as he came strolling into the tiny kitchen.

"Eric was just telling me your gig on *As Time Goes By* has been made permanent. Congratulations."

Ethan shrugged. "For two years, anyway," he said, reaching around Zeke to snag a beer out of the refrigerator. "You going to hang around for the party? Or do you have another secret assignation with America's sweetheart tonight?"

Zeke shook his head and reached for one of the six-packs of beer. "It's over between me and Ariel," he said flatly.

"Since when?"

"Since she showed up at the wrap party last night without the engagement ring I gave her."

"You gave her a ring?" Eric scoffed. "Blackstone the chick magnet and prissy little Chrissy Fortune engaged?"

"No, *not* engaged," Zeke said.

After a moment of silence, Ethan asked, "Does that mean she's on the open market again? Free game?"

Zeke shot him a killing look and stalked out of the kitchen without bothering to answer.

"Jeez, Roberts," he heard Eric say. "Can't you even wait 'til the body's cold?"

Zeke was halfway through his second beer when he heard the music crank up to its usual ear-splitting party volume. "Crimson and Clover" by Tommy James and the Shondells. That meant Eric's ditzy red-headed girlfriend was probably in charge of the music. "Crimson and Clover" was her favorite song; she'd play it over and over if no one objected. After some deliberation, Zeke decided he could stand hearing it three times before he'd be driven to get up off his bed and object. Hopefully, before that happened, someone else would have taken over as DJ for the evening.

He'd just popped the top on his fourth beer when he heard Jack and Eric Shannon arguing in the other bedroom. Something about the option Alan Boyd had offered on their script. Zeke couldn't hear all the words or even most of them, but the tones were crystal clear; the two brothers weren't at all happy with each other. He thought briefly of pounding on the wall to quiet them down but they suddenly stopped on their own, without his interference. Zeke heard the slamming of a door, and then their voices again, still arguing as they went down the hall toward the living room.

That's better, Zeke thought, *now I can hear the music again.*

Steppenwolf's "Born To Be Wild" was shaking the walls now. He liked Steppenwolf.

Somewhere in the middle of his sixth beer, he decided the music was giving him a headache. He got up and stumbled out of his room toward the bathroom, looking for a bottle of aspirin. Somehow, he made a wrong turn and ended up in the kitchen.

"Hey, Zeke, you look like hell, man," Ethan said.

"Feel like hell," Zeke mumbled. "Damn music. Need some aspirin."

"How 'bout a hit instead?" Ethan offered the butt end of a joint between the pinchers of a beaded metal roach clip. "It'll make you forget all about your head."

"No, thanks." Zeke waved the joint away. "I'm too wasted already."

And being wasted wasn't helping in the least. All he could think about was Ariel. She'd been unreasonable, sure. But, hell, he'd been pretty unreasonable too. Maybe, if he thought about it real hard, he could think of a way to patch things up with her. Except, dammit, thinking made his head hurt even worse. What he needed was sleep, he decided. A good night's sleep and then he could tackle the problem of Ariel in the morning with a clear head.

"Goin' to bed," he mumbled and headed back down the hall to his bedroom.

He stopped in the bathroom first—for the aspirin—pausing long enough to empty his overfull bladder and get a drink of water. Then, after stripping down to his skin, he crawled into bed, turned out the light, and passed out cold.

It wasn't until somebody shook him—hard—that he woke up. His mouth tasted like a swamp and his head ached like a son of a bitch but his thought processes were mostly clear. Clear enough, anyway, so he knew "Crimson and Clover" was playing again and there was a woman lying next to him in bed. He'd had one brief moment of intense pleasure, thinking it was Ariel; and then another moment of confusion because the scent and the feel of her was all wrong. And then a light came on, practically blinding him. When his vision cleared, so did the rest of his senses.

It wasn't Ariel in bed with him—he had no idea *who* the naked woman was—but it sure as hell was Ariel standing facing him, looking as if she'd seen a ghost. He'd known, in that split second, that she'd gotten entirely the wrong idea about what was going on. And he knew he had to straighten things out. Immediately.

He vaulted out of the bed.

"This isn't what it looks like," he said, grabbing his pants up off the floor. "Just let me get my jeans on and—"

But Ariel was in no mood to listen to any explanations. She had the bedroom door open before he even got one leg into his jeans.

"Dammit, Ariel, wait a minute. Don't go. I—"

But she was gone.

He hopped around, swearing a blue streak as he yanked his jeans up, leaving them half-unzipped as he went flying out the door after her. Cursing his aching head, cursing the woman in his bed, cursing himself for being so stupid as to have actually tried to drown his sorrows in beer, he chased her down the hall and out into the night. She was as fleet as a damn deer, staying just ahead of him until, suddenly, she stumbled against a chaise longue in the middle of the shadowed courtyard. He thought he might catch her then, but she righted herself in an instant, ignoring the disgruntled comments of the amorous couple who sat up to glare at her, and kept on running.

"Dammit, Ariel. Wait. Please. I can explain, I—" he went down like the proverbial ton of bricks, sprawling over whatever—*whoever*—it was who had tripped him. Some drunk had passed out in the courtyard, he thought as he pushed himself up to his hands and knees.

It was then that he realized he'd landed in something wet and sticky, with an unpleasant smell.

Ah, jeez, he thought in disgust, *the guy's puked all over himself and I fell in it.*

He swallowed hard, trying to keep down the contents of his own abused stomach, and lifted his palms, intending to wipe them off on the drunk's shirtfront. But the stuff on his hands wasn't vomit, it was blood.

He looked down at the man lying sprawled out on the concrete, trying to see his features in the gloom. "Oh, my God," he breathed, his words barely audible over the sudden roaring in his brain.

It was Eric Shannon. Unconscious. Bleeding.

"Oh, my God!" His voice was louder this time. "Call an ambulance," he shouted at the couple on the chaise longue. "Somebody call a damn ambulance!"

THE AMBULANCE finally arrived what seemed like hours later, Zeke remembered, along with the police, but neither of them were able to do Eric any good. He was already dead and had been for quite some time. The police had been relentless in their questioning, but that didn't do Eric any good, either.

Several witnesses said they'd seen or heard Eric arguing with his brother earlier that evening but, then, Eric was always arguing with his brother. Besides, those same witnesses had seen Eric hale and hearty, well *after* Jack had stormed out of the apartment. Other party-goers remembered seeing Eric leave the party in 1-G with his girlfriend, presumably to go upstairs to the apartment she shared with two other girls, but no one could remember the time. The distraught girlfriend confirmed that she and Eric had gone upstairs to be alone but she swore she hadn't seen him take a header over the balcony railing. No one had seen that. At least, no one who was talking.

Through it all, Zeke sat on the chaise longue, bare-chested and bare-footed, smeared with blood and suffering from a mild case of shock. Though required to repeat his story to several different officers—what had he been doing and why was he in the courtyard—Zeke gallantly didn't mention that he'd stumbled over the body while chasing Ariel Cameron as she fled from the party.

That particular piece of information wouldn't have helped the investigation, he thought, because she didn't have anything to do with what had happened. And it wouldn't have been good for Ariel's image to have it known that the darling of *Family Fortune* had been at a loud, boisterous party where alcohol and drugs may have been a major contributing factor in the apparent suicide of one of the young hosts. Unfortunately, several of the other guests saw fit to mention that a major television star was seen running away from the scene of the crime. . . .

"Look, Mrs. Cameron, I know you don't like me. Hell—" Zeke ran his hand through his hair "—I know you hate my guts. But if I could see Ariel, just for a minute," he pleaded. "I could explain the whole thing. I just need to see her."

"My daughter has no desire to see you," Constance Cameron informed him. "She's sick about all of this. Sick and shocked and thoroughly disgusted. Her name in the papers, connected with a sleazy drug party." She shivered with distaste. "Police asking her questions about why she was there. Reporters making nasty insinuations." She fixed him with a malevolent stare. "We both realize, of course, that this sort of sordid publicity is just what you were hoping for all along, from the minute you began your campaign to seduce my daughter."

"No, that's not true, I—"

"Oh, yes, it's very true. I've been onto you from the beginning, Mr. Blackstone. And now Ariel finally sees you for what you are. She's well aware that your image as Hollywood's newest bad boy can only prosper from an incident such as this one. But hers is going to suffer. Maybe quite badly. I've already had a call from one of the network lawyers. He wasn't calling to offer assistance in our time of need," she said. "He was calling to tell me they're seriously thinking about canceling *Family Fortune* for next season." The look she gave Zeke was venomous. "If that happens, my daughter will have you to thank for the ruin of her career."

"I didn't tell the police Ariel was there last night," Zeke said. "I never even mentioned her name. I swear to you, I had nothing to do with the story ending up on the front page of this morning's paper."

"You had everything to do with it," Constance snapped, her voice icy with anger and disgust. "It was your fault she was there at all. Your fault she's been so sickened and shocked by what happened that all she can do is lie in bed and cry."

Zeke felt his heart clench in his chest at the thought of Ariel in tears. Tears *he* had caused. He'd never meant to make her cry. "Let me go up and see her," he begged desperately. "Just for a minute. I promise, I—"

Constance moved in front of him, cutting him off as he started for the stairs. "You won't get around me as easily as you did my daughter," she warned him. "And if you try, if you lay so much as a finger on me in your attempt to invade my home, I'll call the police and have you arrested for trespass and assault."

Zeke hesitated, clearly weighing the consequences of being arrested against the chance of seeing Ariel for a few moments. It would take the police at least five minutes, maybe more, to get there. He could do a lot of explaining in five minutes.

"All right, go on." Constance stepped aside, accurately reading his intent in his eyes. "But you'll only be getting yourself arrested for nothing. Ariel isn't here."

"Not here?" Zeke said suspiciously. "Then where is she?"

"Somewhere where she'll be safe from you."

"Dammit—" Zeke's fists flexed against his sides "— *where is she?*"

"She asked me not to tell you." There was ice-cold triumph in Constance Cameron's eyes. "She pleaded with me, actually, begged me with tears in her eyes not to tell you where she was. I told you, she doesn't want to see you again. Not ever."

BUT *NOT EVER* TURNED OUT to be shorter than anyone could have imagined. Three days later, Zeke received a very legal-looking envelope through the mail slot in the door of apartment 1-G. Inside was an equally legal-looking document, summoning him back to the palatial white mansion in Beverly Hills.

"We've called you here to discuss a matter of some delicacy," the lawyer said when Zeke presented himself at the appointed time. "Before we begin, however, it is imperative that you sign this agreement—" he handed Zeke a pen "—stating that what we discuss here today will go no further than this room."

Zeke looked back and forth between the lawyer and Constance Cameron. "And just what are we discussing?" he asked.

The lawyer inclined his head toward the document.

Zeke put the pen down. "I want to see Ariel first."

"Ariel doesn't want to see you."

"I don't see Ariel, I don't sign." His eyes were hard and implacable as he stared at Ariel's mother. "It's as simple as that."

Without a word, Constance Cameron walked to the door of her fussy, overdone French Provincial office and opened it. "Ask Ariel to come down here, please," she said to whoever was on the other side.

Five minutes ticked by in total silence while they waited for Ariel to appear. When she did, another minute went by before Zeke could bring himself to say anything.

She looked awful. Wan and somehow thinner, although realistically, he knew, she couldn't have lost much weight at all in the four days since he'd last seen her. Her face was pale and there were dark circles under her eyes—and shadows of pain in them. Even her glorious golden hair seemed to have dulled.

Zeke lurched up out of his chair. "Ariel, sweetheart, what has she done to you?"

"What have *I* done to her?" Constance made a harsh sound, somewhere between a bark of laughter and a snort of disbelief. "This is a result of what *you've* done to her."

"What I—"

"Ariel is pregnant."

Zeke's mouth fell open. "Pregnant?"

"Mrs. Cameron, the confidential agreement—" the lawyer began but Constance waved him to silence.

"Pregnant?" Zeke said again, trying to take it in as a half dozen different emotions assailed him at once. Disbelief. Joy. Concern. Pride. Excitement. Confusion. "Is she telling the truth, Ariel?" he asked softly. "Are you really pregnant?"

"Why on earth would I lie about it?" Constance snapped. "Of course, she's pregnant. Do you think we'd be having this distasteful conversation is she weren't?"

"Ariel?" Zeke said, his gaze still riveted to her averted face. She hadn't moved from the doorway, or said a word. Or looked at him. "Ariel, sweetheart..." He had so many questions, he didn't know where to start. When? How? They'd been careful, for the most part, although there had been a time or two ... "How long?" he asked softly.

"Less than six weeks, thank God," Ariel's mother answered. "That makes what we have to do easier."

Zeke shifted his gaze back to Constance. "And what do we have to do?" he asked, his voice low and suddenly dangerous.

"You're going to have to marry her."

Relief flooded through him; he thought she'd meant something else. "Yes, of course," Zeke agreed instantly. "As soon as possible. We'll fly to Vegas or down to Mexico and get married right away. Would you like that, sweetheart?" He held out his hand to her as he spoke, trying to knock down the icy wall she'd erected between them. "We could honeymoon in Acapulco."

She ignored his outstretched hand—and him—as if he didn't exist. "May I go now?" she said to her mother.

Constance looked over her daughter's head at her prospective son-in-law. "Will you sign the agreement?"

Zeke nodded.

"You may go," Constance said to her daughter.

"Ariel, please." Panicked, Zeke reached out and put his hand on Ariel's arm, stopping her. "Don't be this way," he demanded, pleaded. "I love you, dammit. Look at me."

But she stood there, silent as a stone, her slender arm trembling under his fingers, and refused to raise her eyes to his. He wanted to shake her, to make her look at him, but he opened his hand, instead, and let her go, unable to cause her any more pain than she had obviously already suffered. He watched her turn and leave her mother's office without a backward glance, and then he stood, staring at the door for a moment before he turned back to face her mother and the lawyer.

"Where's that agreement you wanted me to sign?"

"Right here." The lawyer handed him the pen again.

Zeke skimmed the brief paragraph and signed. "Is that it?"

"That's just the confidentiality agreement," the lawyer said. "We also have a prenuptial agreement." He laid another sheet of paper on top of the one Zeke had already signed.

Zeke lifted the pen, putting point to paper, and then stopped. "This is just the last page. Where's the rest of it?"

"It's just a standard prenuptial. No need to waste everyone's time reading the entire document now."

Zeke put the pen down. "I guess you'd better send it over to my agent, then. She gets fifteen percent for wasting her time reading entire documents before I sign them." He looked back and forth between Constance and the lawyer. "Is that it?"

The lawyer hesitated, waiting to take his cue from Constance. "That's it for me," he said when she nodded. "Mrs. Cameron would like you to stay for a few moments longer, however." He gathered up the papers on the desk as he spoke and slid them into a black eel skin briefcase. "She has something further she'd like to discuss with you."

"What further?" Zeke asked when the lawyer had gone.

"The wedding."

"Are you sure that's what Ariel wants?"

Constance pounced on that like a cat. "Are you backing out?"

"No, I'm not backing out," Zeke said wearily. "I'm ready to marry Ariel whenever and wherever she wants. If it *is* what she wants."

"What she wants is immaterial to this discussion. She knows what has to be done. And she's agreed to it. She needs a husband and that baby she's carrying needs a father and a legitimate name. Anything less and she can kiss her career goodbye."

"Is that what all this is about? Her damned career?"

Constance raised an eyebrow. "Would you be any less concerned about your career if you were in her position?"

Zeke shrugged, reluctant to answer that because he couldn't refute it. In her position, he *would* be worried about his career. Damn worried.

Public morality might have relaxed to the extent that most people—most people in New York or Los Angeles, anyway—at least accepted the concept of sex outside of marriage. But unwed motherhood still carried a stigma. Especially when your public persona was that of America's fresh-faced little sweetheart.

Zeke sighed and ran his hand through his hair. "When and where?"

"Next Saturday. Right outside these windows on the south terrace." She handed him a five-by-seven file card with a half dozen lines typed on it. "This is the name of a doctor who'll do your blood test and send the results to my lawyer so he can take care of the marriage license. He'll be expecting you to call and set up something for tomorrow. The other name and address is where I've arranged for you to get your tuxedo. You'll need two; one for you and one for your best man. Other than that, all you have to do is show up here no later than twelve-thirty next Saturday, and be prepared to smile your way through this farce."

"Why go to all this trouble?" Zeke asked in amazement, looking down at the card in his hand. "Why not just fly to Las Vegas or Mexico?"

"Because Ariel has an image to live up to," Constance said. "Because America's sweetheart doesn't run off and get married in a tacky Las Vegas wedding chapel or on a beach in Mexico like some dirty hippie. She's going to have a real wedding, with a wedding cake and a maid of honor and a few close family friends as guests. When the wedding photographs are leaked to the press, the world will see that Ariel Cameron married respectably, with the blessing of her mother, and not in some hole-in-the-wall ceremony, as if she had something to be ashamed of."

"And when the baby comes in less than nine months? What happens to all that respectability then?"

"People might count on their fingers, but by then it won't really matter because Ariel will already have been established in the public's mind as a properly married woman."

Zeke could only stare at her. "You've got it all worked out to the last detail, haven't you?"

"Yes, I do. Although, there's one final detail I haven't mentioned yet."

"Which is?"

"After Saturday, I expect you to disappear from Ariel's life for good."

9

"DAD," CAMERON CALLED as Zeke walked into the nave of the church for the wedding rehearsal. "Dad, over here. I want you to meet my bridesmaids. You remember Karen, don't you?" she said, when he was near enough for introductions.

"Yes, of course, I remember Karen." Zeke leaned down to kiss the young woman's cheek. "You were on the cheerleading squad together at Beverly Hills High," he said, making his daughter's friend beam with pleasure to know he really had remembered her.

"And this is Denise, from the office. She's my design partner on the Hoffsteader apartment complex. You know, that renovation project in Exposition Park I told you about?"

"Denise," he said pleasantly, limiting himself to a charming smile and the businesslike handshake she offered. "Cameron's mentioned several times how much she enjoys working with you."

"And this is Michael's best man, Gordon. And his groomsmen, Bruce and Mark and— Oh, Susan, there you are. Finally!" Cameron said on a breath of relief as she broke away from the group and hurried toward her late-arriving maid of honor. "I was beginning to get worried about you."

Zeke stepped back from the crowd of young people a bit as his daughter rushed off to greet her Maid of Honor, unobtrusively drifting away so they could laugh and chat without feeling self-conscious. None of his daughter's friends was in the movie business and, as a result, they tended to stammer and stutter and wonder what to say in the presence of one of Hollywood's biggest and brightest names.

Or maybe, he thought with a sigh, it was just the natural reticence of the young when faced with making conversation with a friend's father.

"Makes you feel old just to look at them, doesn't it?" said a soft voice at his right elbow.

Zeke turned to look down at his ex-wife, surprise clearly written on his face.

"We *did* declare a truce," Ariel said. "Remember?"

One corner of Zeke's mouth lifted in a rueful little smile. "I wasn't sure it would still be in force."

Ariel shrugged, knowing perfectly well what he meant; she hadn't known quite how she was going to face this moment either. "What's a kiss between exes?" she said, having already resolved to treat it lightly.

It had been much more than a kiss, of course, but he wasn't going to argue the point if she wasn't. Not here, anyway. They had Cameron to think of.

He tilted his head toward the chattering crowd of young people, a silent indication that he was going to follow her lead. "How long is this shindig supposed to last?"

The tension in Ariel's shoulders relaxed a degree as she realized he wasn't going to make an issue of what had happened by her pool. "Less than an hour, I hope," she said, glancing at the classic gold Cartier watch on her wrist. "Sondra told me she's made reservations for eight-thirty at La Chaumière for the rehearsal dinner."

"La Chaumière? Is that the restaurant in the Century Plaza Hotel?"

"Yes, it's—"

"Mom. Dad." Cameron squeezed between them, linking an arm in each of theirs. "Everyone is here now, so Leslie thinks we should get started," she said, propelling them back down the wide center aisle toward the rear of the church. She squeezed their arms against her sides, turning to smile up at each of them in turn. "Have I told you both how happy and grateful I am that you're doing this for me?"

Her parents glanced at each other over the top of Cameron's head, the same guilty thought in both their minds. *Grateful?* Their adored only child was *grateful* that her parents were cooperating for her wedding?

"Darling, you don't have to be grateful to us. We're your parents," Ariel said, finding her voice before Zeke had quite managed to swallow the sudden lump in his throat. "You're the most important thing in the world to both of us."

"Oh, I know that," Cameron said breezily, with the self-confidence of a well-loved, well-adjusted child. "It's just that I'm happy to see you together, is all."

"Could we have everyone in the vestibule, please?" the wedding consultant called, beckoning them toward the back of the church with both hands. "We need to get started if we're going to get you out of here on time. No, not you, Michael. You and your best man . . . Gordon, is it? You and Gordon should already be up there—" she waved toward the altar at the front of the church "—with Reverend Nolan. Cameron, dear, you and your bridesmaids need to get in the proper order over here, please."

"Should we have tried to make a go of it for her sake?" Ariel whispered achingly, her gaze pensive and guilt-ridden as she watched Cameron and her bridesmaids scramble to get into position. "Would it have been better for her to have had two full-time parents?"

"She had—*has*—two full-time parents," Zeke said, his gaze soft as he watched his ex-wife watch their daughter.

"But maybe we should have—"

"Look at her," Zeke interrupted gently. "Could she have turned out any better? Be any happier?" Without thinking, he put his arm around Ariel's shoulders and gave her a little squeeze. "We did a good job, sweetheart."

Unconsciously, her eyes still on their daughter, Ariel reached up and touched his hand where it lay on his shoulder. "Yes," she agreed, "in spite of everything, I think maybe we did."

"I *know* we did," Zeke said vehemently, and Ariel turned her head to smile gratefully up at him.

Their eyes met over a distance of inches, a foot at most, and neither of them looked away. If she tilted her head, just a little, it would have been resting on his shoulder. If he tightened his arm, even a tiny bit, she would have been tucked securely against his side. For a moment, both of them ached to do just that.

"Zeke, we need you over here," Leslie Fine said.

And they remembered where they were. And who they were. And what had gone on before. Suddenly self-conscious, like two kids who'd been caught doing something they shouldn't, they averted their eyes and quickly stepped away from each other.

"I'm sorry, Leslie, where am I supposed to be?"

"Standing next to the bride, on her right. Yes, that's fine," she said approvingly, as Zeke bowed from the waist and gallantly offered his elbow to his daughter.

She twinkled up at him. "Maybe you and Mom will turn out to be friends, after all," she said, letting him know she'd seen their brief exchange of glances.

"Maybe." He gave her a sideways look and a small, noncommittal shrug. "Stranger things have happened."

Although, at the moment, he couldn't think of anything stranger than being friends with Ariel. *Friend* was a paltry, lukewarm word to describe the hot, chaotic mix of feelings he felt for his ex-wife. He'd loved her passionately once. Then he'd hated her for a time, just as passionately. For years now, he'd tried not to feel anything for her at all—and most of the time he thought he'd succeeded. But now? One look, one touch, one earth-shaking, brain-numbing, soul-searing kiss, and he was as worked-up and confused as a teenager in the throes of his first love affair.

"We need the mother of the bride at the front of the line with one of the groomsmen," Leslie said briskly.

And Zeke watched Ariel smile her lovely, gracious smile and take the arm of the young groomsman. What was she thinking behind that smile? he wondered. What was she feeling? He didn't know, couldn't tell. Hell, he'd never been able to tell! But he resolved to find out, once and for all, before the evening was over.

"And then the mother of the groom with the other groomsman," Leslie continued, marshaling everyone into order. "That's right. And then, Mr. Everett, if you'll just stand right behind your wife here. That's fine. Now, listen up, everyone. After the soloist has finished singing, there'll be a few moments of quiet and then the organist will start to play. We let a few bars go by, to build up the anticipation, and then we start. Mother of the bride with her escort first, at just a slightly slower than normal walking pace. You'll seat Ms. Cameron on the bride's side of the aisle and take your place next to the best man," she said to the groomsman. "Is that clear?"

The young man nodded.

"When they're about halfway down the aisle, the mother of the groom will start down with her escort, and the groom's father right behind, with the same procedure down at the other end, except that you seat them on the other side of the aisle, with the groom's relatives. The bridesmaids will be next, each of you waiting for my signal to start. And then, when everyone is in place at the front of the church, the first bars of the 'Wedding March' will begin, signaling the guests to stand up and turn to watch the bride. I'll be here to arrange your veil and train, dear, and cue you when to start," she said to Cameron, "and your father will be right by your side to set the pace and keep you going in a straight line, so· all you have to do is smile and look radiant. Has everyone got that? Good, then let's give it a try."

THEY MADE THEIR eight-thirty reservation at La Chaumière with ten minutes to spare, and were immediately seated at a large round table that had been specially set up for them amid the alderwood paneling and eighteenth century French paintings. The dinner was lavish and beautifully served, with silver buckets of vintage champagne and a superlative seafood in lobster saffron sauce that was one of the specialties of the house.

Even at a restaurant like La Chaumière, which wasn't particularly known for celebrity table-hopping, their party managed to attract attention. Three times during dinner people stopped by to say hello and, finding out what the celebration was about, lingered a moment to offer their congratulations to the bride- and groom-to-be. One of the three well-wishers was Tom Selleck, who paused by their table as he entered the restaurant for a quiet dinner with his family. The other two were women.

One was a flashy young starlet in a skintight black Gianni Versace minidress and leopard print stiletto heels. She had achieved a small measure of fame from the part she'd had in Zeke's last movie, and wanted to thank him "one more time" for his part in her success. The other female table-hopper was an elegant soigné French actress who, it was rumored, had once cherished not unfounded hopes of becoming the third Mrs. Blackstone.

"Laure," Zeke murmured, getting to his feet to greet her as she approached the table. They kissed cheeks, three times, in the French way. "What a surprise to see you here," he said, after he had introduced her around the table. "What are you doing in Los Angeles?"

"Business," she said in charmingly accented English. "I may finally be convinced to make an American movie."

"Oh?" Zeke's gaze sharpened with interest. "With whom? And why not with me?"

The actress gave a soft laugh and shook her head. "Not even for you will I be so indiscreet as to name names before it is settled." She gave him an arch look from under her lashes. "When it is all arranged, then I will tell you all about it. Maybe."

"Lunch?" he suggested. "Tomorrow?"

"*C'est selon.*" She lifted one shoulder in an elegant shrug. "I may not know by tomorrow, but you may call me, *oui*?" The look she gave Zeke seemed, to Ariel—

who was sitting across the table watching the exchange—to be rife with suggestion. "I am staying here in the Tower."

"I'll call and we'll set something up," Zeke said.

"Not too early, hmm, *cher ami*?" She reached up and patted his cheek lightly, like a woman who'd made the same gesture many times before. "You know how I like to sleep late." Then, dropping her hand, she turned to smile at the soon-to-be-married couple. "Congratulations on your *mariage*. I wish you much happiness." Her lovely smile widened to include the rest of the people seated around the table. "It was a great pleasure to meet all of you," she said, and lifted her hand in farewell. *"Bon soir."*

The celebration was uninterrupted after that, except for discreet waiters clearing away plates and bringing the *croquembouche*, a classic French wedding cake in the shape of a pyramid, made of cream puffs drizzled with caramelized sugar and decorated with glazed almonds, that had been specially ordered for dessert.

After dinner, in the pleasant confusion of goodbyes and leave-takings, while everyone stood waiting for the various cars to be brought around by the valets, Zeke began to wonder how he was going to maneuver it so that he and Ariel would have some time alone for that discussion he was determined to have with her. The thought of inviting her out for a private drink and being rejected had him as nervous as a schoolboy. And he'd never been nervous around a woman before—not even as a schoolboy. Maybe, instead of asking her out for a drink, it would be better to just follow her home and confront her there. His daughter simplified things by making his move for him.

"Would you mind letting Dad drive you home?" she said to her mother as one of the valets pulled up in the three-year-old red BMW coupe that had been her college graduation present from her father. "Michael and I and the rest of us—" she made a gesture that took in the young bridesmaids and groomsmen "—are going over to this new club in Venice that Gordon says has a great blues band and, well . . ." She shrugged prettily, the wayward child asking a favor of an indulgent parent. "You're in the opposite direction."

"No problem," Zeke said, before Ariel could answer for herself. "I'll be happy to drive your mother home."

"Oh, great! Thanks, Dad," Cameron said, with perhaps a touch more gratitude and enthusiasm than the situation called for. She went up on tiptoe to kiss his cheek, then offered the same caress to her mother. "I'll see you at the dressmaker's on Monday for the final fitting," she said gaily, and then ducked into her car before her mother could say a word in reply.

Ariel stood there for a moment, dumbstruck, and stared after the rapidly disappearing taillights of Cameron's car. Zeke stuck his hands in the front pockets of his Armani slacks and tried not to grin.

"Is it just my imagination," Ariel said, turning to her ex-husband, "or have we just been set up by our own daughter?"

"Oh, surely not," Zeke said, knowing that they had, indeed, been set up. "Cameron's not that devious."

"I don't know." Ariel shook her head slightly. "She made a big deal about how there wasn't any need to drive my car to the church, since she and Michael could pick me up on the way there. And she didn't say a word about going out with her friends after dinner."

"Maybe it was a last-minute thing," Zeke suggested, subtly shouldering the valet out of the way to open the passenger door of the Jaguar for Ariel himself.

"Maybe," Ariel said doubtfully as she slipped into the car.

Zeke took a minute to watch her smooth the skirt of her elegant coral pink suit over her thighs as she settled into the bucket seat, then shut the door and circled around to where another valet already had the driver's door open for him. Ariel turned her head to look at him as he slid behind the wheel, the expression on her face shifting from motherly suspicion to one of maternal concern.

"You don't think Cameron's weaving some sort of ridiculous fantasy about the two of us getting back together after all this time, do you?"

Zeke put the car into gear. "I think the only fantasy Cameron's weaving has to do with us finally being friends," he said as he nosed the Jag out of the parking lot and into the flow of traffic on the Avenue of the Stars.

"Friends?"

"Yeah." Zeke glanced at her out of the corner of his eye, his expression both wry and rueful. "It surprised the hell out of me, too, when she mentioned it."

"She mentioned it?" Ariel demanded. "When?"

"At the church when we were lining up for the procession down the aisle. I guess the fact that you weren't looking through me anymore made her think we might be able to bury the hatchet." The quick look he gave her was speculative and faintly challenging. "Was she right?"

Was she? Ariel wondered as she sat there beside him, wrapped in the dark, artificial intimacy of the car's plush leather interior. Could she be friends with her ex-husband? Did she even want to be? The word *friend* didn't begin to cover all the myriad ways she'd felt about him over the years. Or the way she felt about him now.

"There's been a lot of unhappiness between us," she said, finally.

"There's been a lot of happiness, too," he countered.

Ariel sighed. It was true. Despite everything that had come after, she still remembered that all too brief summer they'd had together as one of the happiest times in her life. She'd been so alive then, as she'd never been before.

Or since.

And it had given her Cameron.

As he said, there'd been a lot of happiness.

But was it enough to make up for the betrayal that had come later?

"Ariel?" he said, when she had been quiet too long.

She sighed again. "We both know we have to come to some kind of understanding, make some kind of peace with the past. For Cameron's sake, if not our own. I'm just not sure how we do that."

"We could go somewhere and talk about it."

"Where somewhere?"

"Jimmy's?" he suggested, naming a popular celebrity haunt that was located between La Chaumière and Ariel's Beverly Hills mansion.

"Good God, no. Ten minutes after we sat down the papers would be printing reconciliation stories and predicting a double wedding."

"Well, then, how about the bar at the Regent Beverly Wilshire? It's discreet and out of the way." Zeke downshifted to take a corner. "Or we could go my place," he added quietly.

"Your place?" Alarm skittered through her at the thought. "You mean the beach house in Malibu?"

Zeke shook his head. "It's still being remodeled. I'm living at the Bachelor Arms right now," he said, and shot her a look to see how she was taking it. Or if she even remembered the name.

Ariel felt her heart jump into her throat. "The Bachelor Arms?" she said faintly. "The same Bachelor Arms where we . . . ?"

"In the very same apartment."

Ariel was silent for a long moment. "I'm surprised that old relic is still standing," she said finally, her voice low and tight with suppressed anger.

Zeke shot her another quick look out of the corner of his eye; he could hear the anger under her calm facade but he didn't have a clue as to what had caused it. "Actually, the building is probably in better shape now than it was twenty-five years ago," he said carefully, feeling his way through what had suddenly become a mine field. "A lot of repair work has been done on it since then."

"Really?" she murmured, her voice dripping ice.

Zeke sighed and ran one hand through his hair. "Look, Ariel, if you don't want to stop by my place for a drink, fine. We won't stop there. But that's no reason to—"

"Dammit, Zeke, just what kind of sick joke are you playing?" she demanded, unable to hold her emotions back any longer.

Zeke looked at her as if she'd suddenly sprouted another head. In all the years he'd known her, he'd never heard Ariel raise her voice. "Sick joke?"

"Did you think if you could maneuver me into going there, I'd be so overcome by the memories that I'd let you seduce me all over again? Is that it?"

"Seduce you?" *God, how do women know these things?* It had only been a half-baked, hopeful idea in his own mind and yet she'd sniffed it out in a second. "Ariel, I—"

"Well, let me tell you something, Zeke Blackstone." She turned in the leather seat to face him more fully, causing the front of her sleekly tailored silk jacket to gape open slightly. "The only memories I have of that third-rate, run-down old apartment building are bad ones," she lied. "Memories of pain and betrayal and heartache. I don't know how you could talk about understanding and friendship one minute, and then suggest that we stop by that awful place the next."

"Look, I'm sorry, all right?" he said, backpedaling for all he was worth and trying not to stare at the exposed edge of her bra. Or, at least, trying not to get caught at it. She still wore white lace underwear, just like she had when she was eighteen. "It was obviously insensitive of me to even suggest it. I just thought—" He ran his hand through his hair again. "Hell, I don't know what I thought!"

But he did know. Sort of. The Bachelor Arms had its bad memories, sure. But most of them were good. And very, very sweet. And he'd thought, if he took her there, that she'd remember some of the good ones with him, and a new understanding would just naturally flow from that. And, oh, all right, he'd been thinking of sex, too, he admitted to himself. Sex was never very far from his mind when he looked at Ariel. It never had been. He'd sort of been hoping that the good memories and the new understanding would lead to renewed intimacy between them. Hell, he was a man, wasn't he?

"So sue me," he muttered under his breath and took another look at Ariel's exposed cleavage, not caring whether she caught him at it or not.

Ariel shot him a fuming look and shifted back around in her seat, facing forward as she yanked the front of her jacket into place. "I think you'd better just take me home," she said, her voice as bland and frosty as a plain vanilla frappé.

She had herself back under control again, Zeke thought with disgust. The brief flash of anger was gone as quickly as it had come. The unflappable, unreachable, remote goddess facade was firmly in place. Zeke vowed he wasn't going to let her get away with it. Not this time, dammit!

He took a deep breath. "I didn't mean to upset you," he said softly, carefully, staring out the windshield of the Jag as he maneuvered through the heavy, late-night traffic on Santa Monica Boulevard. "It's just that the Bachelor Arms holds a lot of good memories for me and I thought—" He shrugged, trying to appear charmingly inept and innocent. "I thought you might feel the same way."

"Well, I don't," she said in a voice calculated to end all conversation then and there. She leaned forward and snapped on the radio to emphasize her lack of desire to talk.

Zeke shrugged and let it go. For the moment. She wasn't going anywhere and, when they got to her place, he wasn't going anywhere, either.

Ariel obviously had a very different idea about how the evening was going to end.

"Thank you for the ride," she said politely, reaching for the handle of the car door as he pulled to a stop on the circular drive in front of the quietly opulent brick mansion. "It was very kind of you to go out of your way."

Zeke's hand shot out and closed over her arm, stopping her from exiting the car. "I didn't do it to be kind, Ariel."

"I'm sure you didn't," she said, pointedly looking down at the large, hair-dusted hand on the sleeve of her chic silk dinner suit. "You're wrinkling my jacket, Zeke."

Very deliberately, he opened his hand and let her go, then reached for the key in the ignition and turned the engine off.

"There's no need to do that," she said as she pushed the car door open. "I'll see myself in."

But Zeke was right behind her as she mounted the wide brick steps to the front door.

Hiding her nervousness behind a well-rehearsed facade of cool indifference, Ariel opened a tiny jeweled evening bag shaped like a flower and took out her house key. She slid it into the brass lock with fingers that shook only slightly, then keyed in a four-digit code to disarm the security system.

"Good night, Zeke," she said dismissively, not even bothering to glance over her shoulder at him as she said it.

"I'm coming in."

Panic fluttered in her stomach but she fought it down. Panic and a strange, tantalizing spurt of what she could only describe as sexual excitement. She fought that down too. "No."

He put his hand on the heavy oak door just above her head and pushed it open, crowding her in ahead of him. "Yes."

"I'll call the police and have you thrown out."

"And risk all the publicity?" He shook his head. "I don't think so, Ariel."

She turned to face him then, cool, slim and imperious as an affronted queen in her chic Yves Saint Laurent dinner suit, matching high-heeled lizard pumps and discreet gold-and-diamond earrings. Her pale gold hair was done up in a sophisticated twist, with a long tendril left to trail down her cheek as if by accident. The expression on her face was icy and impassive, feigning irritation and bored impatience. But her eyes blazed blue fire. Zeke thought she had never looked so impossibly, outrageously sexy. His mouth watered with anticipation.

"All right, then, dammit, come in," she spat out, as if the words left a bad taste on her tongue. "Just don't expect these strong-arm, caveman tactics of yours to change anything."

10

"YOU WANTED to talk." Ariel threw her evening bag into the corner of the plush cream brocade sofa with no thought for its delicacy or cost, and turned to face her ex-husband. "So talk," she demanded imperiously, making no effort to hide her irritation. "I have an early appointment in the morning," she lied, "and I'd like to get to bed at a reasonable hour."

"Aren't you going to offer me a drink first?"

"No." She said the word baldly, almost gleefully, as if daring him to take offense.

Zeke shrugged and walked over to the crystal decanters arranged on a silver tray atop an elegant eighteenth-century cherrywood sideboard. There was a selection of Waterford crystal bar glasses on the narrow shelf above the decanters and a small refrigerator with an automatic ice maker tucked behind the cupboard doors below. "Can I pour something for you?" he asked politely, as he helped himself to a weak bourbon and soda with lots of ice.

"Scotch. Straight," she said, surprising him. The Ariel of old hadn't been much of a drinker. She'd only had one glass of champagne at dinner tonight—and then only finished half of it.

Grinning to himself, he poured two fingers of Scotch into the bottom of a heavy cut crystal tumbler, then turned and held it out to her. The look in his dark eyes dared her, telling her without words that he didn't think she would really drink it.

She surprised him again.

Grabbing the glass out of his hand, she tossed back half of the contents in one gulp, then set it down—sharply—on the delicate cabriole-legged table at the end of the sofa and glared at him, her eyes watering from the fierce sting of the alcohol. "There. We've had a drink. Satisfied? Now say what you have to say and then please leave."

Zeke took a casual sip of his own drink. "Do you want to tell me what you're so damned mad about?"

"You forced your way into my house, isn't that reason enough?"

"You were mad at me before I did that. In fact," he said, just realizing it himself, "you've been quietly furious at me since that day at the wedding consultant's office. Why is that, I wonder?" he said musingly, watching her closely for a reaction.

She just stood there, staring daggers at him, her slender body as tense and straight as an arrow quivering against the string of a drawn bow, looking more beautiful and desirable than he'd ever seen her look before.

"Before that day we hadn't seen each other in—what?—three, almost four years? At Cameron's college graduation ceremony, remember? And we didn't speak to each other, even then. So, I have to wonder . . ." His dark gaze locked on hers, penetrating, demanding. "Why are you so angry?"

"I'm not angry, I'm—" Ariel turned her back on him and walked toward the multipaned, leaded glass doors that opened out onto the patio and pool. Her shoulders lifted in a deep, shaky sigh he heard halfway across the room. And then she put her hands on the glass, palms flat against the surface.

"Talk to me, Ariel," he said from behind her.

She sighed again and turned around to face him. "I'm not angry," she said, but her voice wasn't as crystal cool and calm as it normally was, even to her own ears. And the fire in her eyes hadn't quite been banked. And her smooth, alabaster cheeks were delicately flushed with emotion.

"Oh, you're angry, all right," he taunted her, trying to get at the source of her pent-up emotion. "You're so angry, you're seething with it. You're boiling inside, aren't you, Ariel? You'd like to tear me apart with your bare hands, wouldn't you?"

He put his drink down on the sideboard and stepped closer, as if inviting her, daring her, to reach out and do some violence to his person. She clenched her hands at her sides and refused to give him—or herself—the satisfaction of losing control.

He extended one hand and she stepped back, automatically trying to avoid his touch, but he only picked something up off the table behind her. Then he reached out and grabbed her wrist with his other hand, quickly, before she could jerk away from him. Turning it palm up, he forced her to unclench her fingers and pressed something cold and round and hard into her hand.

It was one of her collection of glass and crystal paperweights, the sapphire-blue Lalique with the swirl of real gold dust through the middle.

Her fingers curled around it, so tightly that her knuckles showed white.

"Go, ahead," Zeke whispered. "Throw it."

She hesitated, her whole body trembling with the need to release the feelings that had been locked up inside her for so long.

"Pretend you're aiming at my head."

With a muffled shriek of pure, unadulterated rage, Ariel lifted the fragile paperweight and heaved it at the wall with every ounce of strength she possessed. It shattered on impact, splintering into a thousand glimmering shards with a sound like a rifle shot across the water. She stood, stock-still, breathless, panting, her unbelieving gaze riveted on the dent she'd made in the pale blue watered-silk wall covering. *My God, I did that,* she thought, aghast at her action. She'd never lost control like that in her life, not even when Zeke had broken her heart and shattered her dreams. She never raised her voice. Never lost her temper. Never forgot who she was, not even for one minute. Never.

"Feel better now?"

Ariel turned to look at her ex-husband. He stood there, watching her with a little half smile on his handsome face, his stance casual under the elegant, loose-fitting Armani suit, the expression in his dark eyes expectant and faintly... amused.

He was laughing at her!

"No, dammit, I don't feel better," she snarled, furious as a spitting cat.

But it was a great, big, whopping, bald-faced lie. She felt marvelous. She felt vital and alive. Hot, surging emotion was roiling through her like a violent thunderstorm over a calm mountain lake, churning everything up. For the first time in her controlled, circumspect life, she let it spill out.

"Why did you do it?" she demanded, her voice low and furious.

"Do what?"

"Sleep with that woman."

For a moment, Zeke looked blank, truly not understanding what woman she was referring to, then comprehension dawned. She could only mean one woman, after all.

"All I did that night was sleep with her," he said, emphasizing the verb. "And I didn't even know I was doing that until I woke up to find you standing there, staring at me as if I'd just committed murder."

She made a dismissive gesture with one hand. "Don't lie to me, Zeke," she said impatiently. "Not now. Not after all these years. I saw you, remember? I was there, in the room with you and I saw—"

"What did you see?" he demanded.

"I saw . . ." Memories of that night formed a picture in her mind's eye. The way she'd reached down in the dark to touch him and had touched the naked shoulder of the woman in bed with him, instead. The husky female voice offering to wake him up. The sexy tumble of chestnut curls and sleep-flushed skin when the light came on. The naked bodies. Two of them.

She looked Zeke straight in the eye, daring him to deny it. "I saw everything I needed to see."

"The hell you did. You saw me sleeping. *Sleeping,*" he emphasized. "And then you ran away without giving me a chance to explain."

"Because there was nothing to explain!" she shouted, and then, shocked at her own behavior, she covered her face with her hands to keep from seeing the startled expression on his. "There was nothing to explain," she repeated in a more normal tone of voice. "I guess there never is, in a situation like that." She gave a strangled, embarrassed laugh and dropped her hands, the vital,

energized feeling of a moment ago abruptly deserting
her.

"I didn't have sex with her," Zeke said softly, willing
her to believe him. "No, dammit—" he reached out and
grasped her chin when she tried to turn away "—look
at me. I did *not* have sex with her. I didn't even know
who she was until later."

"Then what was she doing in your bed?"

"I don't know." Zeke let go of her chin to run his hand
through his hair. "I swear to God, Ariel, I don't really
know. I don't think she really knew, either. She was still
there after the police left that night, stoned out of her
mind on something. Maybe she just wanted a place to
sleep it off. Hell, maybe she was just into indiscrimi-
nate sex the way too many people were back then and
thought I might be a likely candidate. All I know is that
I was alone when I went to sleep and when I woke up,
there she was."

"And you're telling me nothing happened?"

"Not unless she took advantage of me while I was out
cold," he said, trying to inject a little humor into the
situation. He could tell by the expression on Ariel's face
that the attempt had fallen sadly short. "I was more
unconscious than asleep that night," he said seriously,
with no attempt at humor this time. "I'd drunk a lot of
beer before I finally passed out. So if she expected anything when she crawled into bed with me, she was disappointed. I couldn't have gotten it up if I'd wanted to."

"It doesn't matter," Ariel said, wondering if it did.
Why it did. "I guess none of it really matters now. I
don't know why I even brought it up."

"You brought it up because you needed to know," he
said. "And I needed to tell you. I still need to tell you."

"Tell me what?" Ariel whispered.

"I was all torn up because you hadn't worn my ring at the wrap party for *Wild Hearts*. You were so cool and polite. So damned distant. You wouldn't even look at me except when the photographers asked us to pose for pictures. I figured it was your way of telling me it was really over between us. That you'd decided you couldn't bring yourself to publicly admit America's sweetheart was involved with a roughneck small-time actor from New York." His shrug was rueful and self-deprecating.

"That's why I got so drunk that night. I was trying to drown my sorrows and ended up passing out. When I woke up, there she was. And there you were. I never did figure out *why* you were there, you know," he said reflectively. "I thought, later, that it must have been because you'd found out you were pregnant and wanted to tell me you'd changed your mind about getting married because of it. But if that had been the case, then why did you refuse to see me the next day?" He shook his head as if her behavior still puzzled him. "That never made any sense to me."

Ariel's blue eyes widened a fraction. "You tried to see me the next day?"

"As soon as I could. But I barely made it through your front door. Your mother said you were shocked and disgusted with me and everything that had happened. The reporters had been hounding you about Eric's suicide and the network execs had made some not so subtle threats about canceling your show. She said you weren't home and that you'd begged her not to tell me where you were."

"No, I didn't. I . . ." Ariel shook her head.

"Are you telling me that's not true? That your mother lied?"

"I don't know," she admitted hesitantly, knowing full well that her mother might very well have lied to him. And to her. All in the name of protecting her daughter, of course. "I might have said it." She shook her head again. What good would it do to revile her mother now? Constance Cameron had been dead for nearly ten years, and they had been estranged for nearly ten years before that because Ariel had refused to let Constance run Cameron's life.

"I probably did say it. Or something close to it," Ariel said, finally. "When I left the Bachelor Arms I was borderline hysterical. I could barely see to drive home, I was crying so hard. And then I smashed my car into the corner of the garage and whacked my forehead on the steering wheel when I got there because I was shaking so much that I couldn't steer straight."

He reached out, as if to touch her head where she'd hit it, and she stepped back, quickly, evading his touch. If he touched her right now, she'd collapse into a small, pitiful heap of blubbering, incoherent emotion. And she needed to get this out first. She'd been carrying it around inside for far too long.

"My mother was upset, of course, wanting to know where I'd been and what happened to put me in such a state. And then the police showed up, asking me what I knew about Eric Shannon's death. And...I really don't know." She spread her hands in front of her, palms up. "Maybe I suffered some kind of shock or emotional trauma because nothing is really clear until a day or two later when I woke up in a hospital bed."

"My God, Ariel. I'm sorry. I had no idea."

"It wasn't serious. The car accident, I mean. Just a dented fender and a bump on the head. I could have been home in my own bed, except that my mother was always so overprotective. I was her only child." She smiled ruefully. "Her precious single chick."

Her meal ticket, Zeke thought.

"She was used to taking care of me, of being everything to me, and doing everything for me." It had been an unhealthy relationship—Ariel knew that now—a way for Constance to control and live through her daughter. But Ariel had trustingly accepted it, unaware there was any other kind of mother-daughter relationship until her own tiny daughter was born.

"She was frantic with worry that I might have been seriously hurt and she wanted me to be checked over thoroughly," Ariel explained, "just to make sure I was all right. That's when I found out I was going to have a baby. The doctor told me when I woke up."

"Then you didn't go to the Bachelor Arms that night because you were pregnant."

"No. I went because I . . ." Her voice trailed off. Why bring it up now, twenty-five years later? Nothing she could say would change what had happened. Nothing would bring back those lost years.

"Because you what?" Zeke insisted gently, watching her with dark, eager eyes.

"Because I wanted to tell you that I'd changed my mind. That you were more important to me than my career or my image as America's sweetheart. That, despite my doubts, I'd marry you whenever you wanted, without waiting to see if my contract had been renewed or not, regardless of what my mother said. No, don't," she said, when he reached for her. "Please don't."

But Zeke ignored her, drawing her into his arms and against his chest, holding her close as he had wanted to do that fateful night. And so many nights since. "I'm sorry," he crooned. "I'm so sorry, sweetheart."

She realized then, as she stood there with her face pressed against his broad chest, that she was crying. She could feel the wetness against her cheek, soaking into the silk of his shirt. She could feel his heartbeat, solid and strong, and her own, beating wildly in answer. She could feel his arms around her, warm and comforting; his breath, soft as a whisper against her temple; his big hands, rubbing slowly, soothingly, up and down the length of her spine. He meant his arms to be comforting, she knew, and his touch to be soothing, but she could feel the vibrant life and vitality and passion coming back into her body, called into being by the searing heat and virility of his.

She wanted to curl her fingers into the smooth, silky fabric beneath her hands and hold on for dear life. She wanted to burrow her face into his hard, comforting chest and bawl like a baby. She wanted to melt into him until neither of them knew where one began and the other ended. She wanted, desperately, to surrender to her feelings and the moment, giving free rein to everything he stirred in her and responding to every single thing he made her feel. She wanted to feel *alive* again, if only for one night.

She lifted her head from his chest, pushing back enough to look up into his face. "Zeke," she murmured, her voice husky and compelling. "Kiss me."

He looked down into her face for a long moment, the expression on his own a mixture of surprise and banked desire. And then he bent his head and touched his lips, very lightly, to hers.

It wasn't at all the kind of kiss she had in mind.

"No," she said, and slid her hands up over his chest to curl them around the back of his neck. "Really kiss me."

Zeke felt a bolt of pure electricity shoot down his spine, but he held himself back, remembering what had happened out by the pool when he'd recklessly given in to the needs she stirred in him. "The last time I 're-ally' kissed you, you made a pretty snide remark about my sexual habits."

"I'm sorry." She blushed, a combination of nerves and embarrassment. And excitement. "Your sexual habits are none of my business."

"Well, actually—" one corner of his mouth turned up in a wry, self-mocking, unconsciously sexy little grin "—if you intend to take this much further than a kiss, you'd better make it your business." He waited a beat but she didn't respond.

He wondered if he'd misread her intent, but she didn't move or draw away. She just stood there, looking up at him with a burning light in her eyes he'd never seen before.

Still, he hesitated, wanting but unsure. What was she really asking for? Was it just sex or something deeper? Was he going to end up with his heart all battered and broken again?

She started to draw away. "If you don't want me . . ."

"No." His arms tightened, holding her where she was. "I want you. God knows, I want you. I've *always* wanted you." He pressed his mouth to hers.

It was exactly the kind of kiss she wanted. Exactly. Hard and hot and ravenous. His tongue invaded her mouth, thrusting boldly, taking what she so desperately needed to give, gathering up her sweetness and her heat, then giving it back tenfold. He licked at her lips, ran his tongue over the edge of her teeth, touched it to the sensitive roof of her mouth, telling her without words how urgently he desired her. It was a rapacious, voracious, eating kiss that went on . . . and on . . . and on . . . until her brain evaporated and her body melted against his. And still he kissed her, tasting, savoring, appreciating all the delicate tastes and textures of her willing mouth, seducing her into mindless, aching need with his kiss alone. She whimpered softly and pressed against him, needing more. So much more.

Without taking his mouth from hers, he slid one hand between them and released the two gold buttons on the front of her chic St. Laurent suit, then put his hands on her shoulders, blindly forcing her arms down from around his neck as he pushed the jacket off. As soon as it slid over the ends of her fingers, she put her hands back on his chest and slid them up and over his broad shoulders, under his jacket, pushing it down his arms to the floor. Catching his hands in hers, she lifted them to her lace-covered breasts, unable to wait another minute for him to do it on his own.

He cupped her breasts in his palms, squeezing gently. She moaned and bit his bottom lip, not quite as gently. He kneaded her through the lace of her bra, drawing his fingers together around the tip of each turgid nipple, making her gasp with pleasure against his lips. And then doing it again. And again. And again.

It was too much . . . too much. And not nearly enough. The heat in her was furnace hot now, intemperate and needy. So very, very needy. Mindless with the heat, she reached down and placed her hand over the hard bulge beneath the fly of his elegant Armani slacks.

He groaned and thrust himself into her palm, reaching down to press her hand more firmly against him for a moment. She curled her fingers beneath his and squeezed. Zeke stiffened and pulled her hand away, fighting for the control that was rapidly slipping away.

He had meant to use all the finesse at his command. He had meant to seduce and captivate and delight her with prolonged kisses and soft, lingering caresses. But her bold, hungry touch had pushed him over the edge. He was on fire. His heart felt like a blast furnace in his chest, burning up his brain, sending his blood sizzling through his veins, racing headlong down a path that led directly to his groin. And there was only one way to put it out. He had to have her. Now.

"I hope to God you're ready for me," he murmured raggedly, reaching around her for the zipper on her skirt.

But he needn't have worried. Ariel—cool, calm, collected Ariel—was already yanking at the plain gold buckle on his snakeskin belt. Clothes fell around them like leaves in a high wind. Her skirt. His shirt. Her bra. His pants. Shoes were kicked off, socks and stockings and underwear peeled down and cast aside without a thought for modesty or decorum.

Naked, they came together, heat against heat, body against body, straining, eager, hot, sinking down onto the cream brocade sofa without regard for the costliness of the fabric beneath them. He kissed her neck and the soft curve of her shoulder. She kissed his chest and the hard curve of his biceps. And then he slipped his hand down, between her legs, unable to wait a moment longer, and found her. She was soft and wet, as swollen as if the foreplay had lasted long, maddening hours rather than just a few heated moments. She whimpered and shifted under him, tilting her pelvis up like an offering. He groaned and shifted on top of her, settling his hips between her thighs. There was a moment's fumbling intensity, a tentative probing, a gentle stretching, and then he was seated to the hilt.

She moaned.

And he moaned.

And then they both began to move. It was hard and fast. Primitive. Basic. Powerful. Frantic. Muscles straining. Nerves screaming. Every feeling raw and exposed. They rolled off the sofa and onto the thickly carpeted floor, still holding tight, still thrusting against each other, still wild with the need to get closer. And then closer still.

He couldn't thrust hard enough.

She couldn't take him deep enough.

And then they came suddenly, explosively, within seconds of each other, splintering apart like the crystal paperweight, shattering, thousands of shards of heat and emotion hurtling through them at breakneck speed.

Ariel's whole body bowed under the strength of her climax. Her back arched, high and taut, the muscles in her neck and chest and abdomen strung tight with voluptuous tension. She dug her heels into the carpet, thrusting her pelvis upward in a mindless effort to force him deeper. She gave a high keening cry and sunk her manicured nails into his taut buttocks to hold him close.

Zeke roared like a wounded beast as his orgasm claimed him. His upper body arched up and away from hers, the muscles of his arms and chest and shoulders bulging and straining with the exquisite pleasure of release. His hips pressed down, driving her deeper into the carpet. His fists clenched in the hot, silky strands of her hair. It seemed to go on . . . and on . . . and on, keeping both of them balanced on the very pinnacle of sublime, intemperate, torturous feeling, wringing every last drop of passion from them.

And then Zeke collapsed against her, muttering hot, breathless hosannas to satisfaction and passion, and wrapped his arms around her, crushing her slender body to his sweating, heaving chest. And she slid her arms around his back, holding him tight as hot tears of spent passion trickled from the corners of her eyes.

There was a moment's quiet as they held each other, the silence filled only with their soft panting breath and the rapid pounding of two hearts. And then Zeke raised his head from the curve of her neck and smiled down into her eyes.

"I've always said it's better when you're in love," he whispered.

11

FOR A MOMENT it was as if she had been catapulted back in time.

Suddenly, it was twenty-five years ago and she was eighteen and desperately in love, hearing those hoarsely whispered words for the very first time. Everything was so much the same as it had been then. The heat and hardness of his lean, naked body above hers. The trembling, unfamiliar weakness of her own. The warm, panting sweetness of utter completion. The big, hard hands tenderly brushing back the tendrils of hair from her damp face. The soft, caressing, awestruck look in his eyes as he smiled, oh so tenderly, into her eyes.

For a moment—just a sweet, painful, exquisitely delicious moment—she let herself believe it completely. Let herself luxuriate in the fantasy that he truly meant his softly whispered words of love.

And maybe he did.

For the moment.

But the moment wouldn't last.

It hadn't then and it wouldn't now.

No matter how much she wanted to believe it would.

"It's never been this way with anyone else," Zeke whispered. His voice was fervent and sincere, tinged with the wonder of his feelings and the magic of the moment.

But he had sounded sincere the last time, too, Ariel reminded herself. And awestruck. And earnest. And look what had happened. Resolutely, she steeled her heart against the hot, sweet rush of emotion that flooded her. Against the desperate desire to believe he really meant what he said. Because to believe again— and have that belief shattered—would destroy her.

Zeke brushed his lips against her cheek, reverently, sweetly, kissing away the lingering traces of passion's tears. "In all these years, no one has ever made me feel the way you do," he whispered, his voice as soft and sweet and cherishing as his kisses. "Not once in twenty-five years."

"Oh, Zeke," she murmured raggedly, unable to endure another word. "Don't." She clenched her fists against his back, fighting the soul-deep longing to succumb to the almost irresistible lure of his pretty, meaningless words of love. Words she was sure he had uttered a hundred times before, to a hundred different women. "Please don't."

His body tensed, infinitesimally, above hers. "Don't?" he said softly, his lips still pressed against her cheek.

"Don't say what you think I want to hear. I don't want to hear it," she lied. *Not unless you really mean it.* "I don't need to hear it."

"Don't need to hear what?"

"The pretty words. The sweet lies. The—"

"Lies?" He lifted his head to look down at her. "You think I'm *lying* to you?"

"I know you don't think of it as lying. And maybe it isn't, exactly." It was, she supposed, just another part of his roguish charm, a way of making a woman feel special and wanted, his way of saying thank you for pleasures exchanged. "But it isn't the truth, either. It's just—" She closed her eyes, unable to bear another moment of looking into his, afraid the puzzled sincerity in his gaze would make her believe against her own better judgment. "It's just the mood. The heat of the moment. You don't really mean it," she whispered achingly. "It's just the sex talking."

He pushed himself up on his hands to stare down at her. "Just sex?" he said, incredulous and insulted. "You think this is just about sex?"

She opened her eyes and looked up at him. "Isn't it?" she challenged softly.

Zeke stared down at her for a long moment, his biceps bulging as he braced himself above her, his sex still sheathed in her body, his hot, dark gaze roving over her face, taking in the blatant distrust and doubt in her expression. She really didn't believe him! How could she not? How could she lie there beneath him, with their bodies still intimately joined, still damp and heated with the wild passion of their loving, their hearts still pounding with the emotional upheaval of what had happened between them, and think he was *lying* to her about his feelings?

"I love you, Ariel," he said fiercely, willing her to believe it, to accept it. "I've never said that to another woman. Ever."

But she only lay there, looking up at him with tear-bright, disbelieving eyes, and said nothing.

With a strangled oath, he pushed himself up and off her, grabbing her by the upper arms and dragging her to her knees as he reared back on his. He wanted to shake her until her teeth rattled. How could she not believe him? How could she not see the truth of how he felt about her? How could she—

But she had done it before. Twenty-five years ago she had heard his words of love and not believed them. *Refused* to believe them.

"Why?" he demanded, suddenly furious. And suddenly, deeply hurt. No woman had ever made him feel that way before, either, as if his guts were being ripped out while he watched. No woman except Ariel. He shook her once, hard. "Tell me why, dammit!"

But she clamped her lips together and lowered her lashes, refusing to speak.

Her refusal to talk only fueled his fury, reminding him of the day in her mother's office, when he'd been callously informed he was about to become a father and a bridegroom. She had refused to speak to him then, too, making him feel guilty and ashamed for something that should have been beautiful.

"Is it because it's only sex for you?" he demanded, wanting to hurt her as much as she had hurt him. Then and now. "Is that it? A little tumble with the ex-husband to see if he's still got what it takes to make America's sweetheart howl like a bitch in heat?"

She shook her head, still unable to speak through the lump in her throat. Her lips began to tremble, despite the way she had them clamped together. A tear leaked out from under her tightly closed lashes.

Zeke watched the tear trickle down her cheek and felt like an emotional terrorist. "Oh, God, Ariel, don't," he murmured, aghast at what he'd done. "Don't cry, sweetheart. I'm sorry. I didn't mean that. You know I didn't."

"I hate this," she murmured brokenly, reaching up with one hand to dash at the tears on her cheek. "God, I hate this."

Zeke went very still. "What do you hate?"

"Crying. Losing control. Falling apart." She opened her eyes, finally, when she had her tears under control, and looked at him. "Feeling so damned needy and desperate. I've been doing just fine for years. I've had Cameron and my work. A nice tidy social life. I've had everything under perfect control. And then you come back into my life and . . ." She made a helpless, fluttering gesture with her hands, and her eyes, as she stared at him, were full of accusation. " . . . and, just like that, I fall in love with you all over again, and everything goes straight to hell."

"Ariel," he said, a wide, beatific smile blooming on his handsome face. He looked as if he'd just won an Oscar and the California lottery combined.

"No, don't." She put her hands against his chest, stopping him when he would have pulled her back into his arms. "Don't."

"But you love me. You just said so. And I love you."

"Love isn't enough. It wasn't then, and it isn't now."

"Maybe not then," he agreed, hearing only what he wanted to hear. "Back then we were just a couple of stupid kids who let our insecurities get in the way of what we had. But it will be different this time," he assured her jubilantly, feeling as if he could take on the world single-handedly and win, "because we're different."

Ariel shook her head, refusing to let herself be swept up in his emotions. "I don't want to be in love with you, Zeke." She pulled back, shrugging out from under the hands that gripped her upper arms. "Don't you understand? I won't *let* myself be in love with you. Not again."

"You already are in love with me."

"Then I'll get over it."

"Will you?"

"Yes. Yes, dammit, I will!" She reached around behind her as she spoke, searching through the haphazardly strewn clothing for something to cover herself with. His forest green silk shirt came to hand first and she dragged it onto her lap. "I can't go through it again, Zeke," she said, her head down as she struggled to turn it right-side out. "I can't take another betrayal. I won't. It hurts too much."

"You weren't the only one who was hurt," he said quietly. "Or betrayed."

She looked up, her eyes widening at the injustice of that. The shirt was forgotten, the struggle with the tangled sleeves abandoned. "I didn't betray you. Not once. Not ever."

"You chose your mother and your career over me."

Her fists clenched in the pile of silk on her lap and she dragged it up, holding it to her bare breasts like a shield. "Only after I found you in bed with another woman," she said fiercely.

He remembered the sequence of events a bit differently but decided to let it pass in favor of more important issues. "I thought we'd already established my innocence on that point. I didn't have sex with that woman. I didn't even know her."

"With how many others, then?" she burst out, unable to hold the words back. They'd been roiling around in the back of her mind for twenty-five long years.

He stared at her for a long moment. "There were no others," he said, finally. "Not from the first day I met you on the set. There was only you."

"And the script girl, and the hairdressers, and the makeup artist's assistant, and the waitresses in the studio cafeteria and—"

"What the hell are you talking about?"

"You! I'm talking about you and your harem."

"My harem?"

"Your legions of adoring women. The ones who hang on your every word, who swoon at your slightest glance. The waitresses, the secretaries, the production assistants, your leading ladies. That professional femme fatale who stopped by the table at dinner this evening. The lovely Laure Montigny, whose sleeping habits you're all too familiar with. Holly Neals. Kathy Billings," she said, naming his second ex-wife and the actress who'd sued him—unsuccessfully—for palimony. "That Italian countess who was living in your New York apartment last year. The councilwoman who almost lost the election because of rumors that the two of you were using her office for more than meetings about censorship. The lingerie model who told the tabloids all about your taste in women's underwear. The stunt woman who—"

"Well, I'll be damned," Zeke interrupted, flabbergasted by her heated recital of his past relationships. Or his past relationships according to the tabloids, anyway. He'd have been dead of exhaustion if he'd actually been with that many women. He didn't know whether to be flattered or annoyed that she'd kept such close track of his alleged affairs. "You're jealous."

"No," Ariel said despondently, knowing all along that he would misunderstand. "No, I'm not jealous. I'm afraid."

"Afraid? Afraid of what?"

"Of you and your insatiable need for women."

"I don't need *women*," he said in exasperation. "I need one woman. You."

"And I need security. I need to know that the man I love will be faithful, that I can trust him. I can't trust you." She looked him straight in the eyes as she spoke the next words. "I never could."

It took him a minute to tamp down the roiling surge of anger her words engendered. "I never cheated on you, Ariel," he said, when he could speak calmly. "Not once. Not that summer while we were making *Wild Hearts*. Not during the entire time we were married."

Her eyes widened, disbelief and hope warring in their fathomless blue depths.

"You were my wife, pregnant with my child, and I'd made a vow to be faithful." He smiled ruefully and reached out, gently tucking a loose strand of hair behind her ear, the way he had years ago, when it used to hang down to her waist. "I kept hoping you'd change your mind and decide to make it a real marriage, and I didn't want anything to stand in the way of that possibility, especially not another woman who couldn't even begin to mean to me what you did. What you still do."

"But you were forced to marry me."

"No one forced me to do anything, except leave you right after the wedding pictures were taken. I'd already asked you to marry me, remember? There was no force involved."

"But the lawyers . . ." She frowned, trying to remember the exact sequence of events in that chaotic, painful time of her life. "My mother said she had to threaten you with lawyers. That you wouldn't have gone through with it otherwise."

"And you believed her?"

"Yes, I believed her."

"Even though you knew she despised me and the fact that we'd had a relationship?"

"She was my mother. My only living relative. And I was eighteen years old, scared and pregnant, and I thought you'd betrayed me."

He was silent a moment, absorbing that, accepting the truth of it. "I didn't," he said simply, honesty shining out of his dark eyes like a beacon. "You've got to believe that, Ariel. I never betrayed you."

"I do believe it. Here," she said, lifting one hand to lightly touch her temple. "But in here—" she dropped her hand to her chest, pressing it over the silk shirt she held clutched in front of her heart "—I'm still afraid."

"Because you still don't trust me to be faithful?"

"Because I don't trust . . . us," she said, avoiding the exact, bald-faced truth in favor of a lesser, more tactful reality. "I don't trust all the roller coaster emotions. I don't like the feeling of being out of control, of not knowing what's going to happen next. It's all happened too fast for me. Way too fast."

Zeke smiled at that, the curve of his lips rueful. "It's been twenty-five years in the making, sweetheart."

Ariel shook her head. "Those were two other people, in a whole other time. You and I just met a few short weeks ago. In that time we've barely exchanged two dozen civil words to each other and, yet, here we are..." She lifted one hand, palm up, indicating the strewn clothes, and the two of them. " . . . naked on the living room floor."

"And that scares you?"

"*Yes,*" she said fervently. "Doesn't it scare you?"

He thought about it for a moment. "Yeah," he said slowly. "Come to think of it, it does. A little. What do you think we could do to make it a little less frightening?"

"We could slow down," Ariel said. "We could take the time to get to know each other...I won't say 'again' because we really didn't know each other before. We could—"

"Go steady?" Zeke suggested, feeling suddenly lighthearted. She wasn't proposing an end, as he'd been half-afraid she would, but a beginning.

"How about if we start by dating first?" she suggested.

"All right," he agreed promptly, making her smile. "Have lunch with me tomorrow."

"I thought you were planning on having lunch with Laure Montigny?" she said, before she could stop herself.

"Those plans were tentative. And strictly business." He reached out and lifted her chin with his curled finger, forcing her to look at him. "Despite what the tabloids have said, the only thing between Laure and me is friendship. And the only reason I happen to know she likes to sleep late is because of that movie we did a couple of years ago for Louis Malle. She used to bitch like hell whenever she had to do a scene before noon. So..." He let the back of his finger trail down the front of her throat before dropping his hand. "...lunch tomorrow?"

"All right," she said softly. "Lunch tomorrow. Someplace discreet," she added, hurrying on to explain before he could ask. "I don't want to give the tabloids any grist for the mill, not with Cameron's wedding only a week away."

Zeke was silent for a moment, digesting that. "Are we going to tell Cameron about this?"

Ariel bit her lip, unsure of how he would take what she was going to say. "I'd rather not. Not yet. Not until we know what, or if, anything's going to change between us. It wouldn't be fair to raise her hopes. Especially not now, when she's got so much else on her mind. This is *her* time, not ours."

Zeke nodded, accepting the wisdom of that. He was sure things were going to change between them, and change drastically, but Ariel was right. Cameron's wedding came first right now, and nothing would be allowed to overshadow or spoil it. He'd be a gentleman, keeping things low-key and discreet until Cameron was safely wed and away on her honeymoon. But after that, all bets were off. He wanted Ariel back, and he was going to get her.

"I know just the place for our first date," he said. "It's small, out of the way and very discreet."

"NICE PLACE," Ariel commented as they entered the neighborhood bar the next afternoon. The decor was primarily black-and-white, rather Art Deco in feeling, with polished brass railings and dark wood to soften the color scheme and keep it from appearing too stark. The walls were lined with framed publicity stills from the twenties and thirties, most notably Errol Flynn and other big male stars of the era. "It's just what the doctor ordered," she said as they settled themselves into one of the booths that ran along the wall. "Small, out of the way and—"

"So much for discretion," Zeke muttered, catching sight of the young blond waitress who was hurrying over to greet them. They were about to be recognized.

"Mr. Blackstone," she said, her face lighting up with obvious pleasure at the sight of him. "Welcome to Flynn's."

"Actually, it's Smith." He tugged the bill of his black L.A. Raiders cap down so it shadowed his face and hunched one shoulder, doing a deliberately bad imitation of a movie undercover cop trying not to be recognized. "John Smith. And that's my snitch." He gestured toward Ariel, who sat across from him, hiding behind a pair of large, tinted sunglasses that obscured most of the top half of her face. "Ruby LaSalle."

Bobbie-Sue O'Hara didn't miss a beat. "Well, Mr. Smith. Ms. LaSalle," she said, just as if she'd hadn't recognized the famous television actress. "What can I get you to drink?"

"I'll have a beer. Miller Lite. Ruby?"

"A glass of Chablis."

"And could we get some of those pretzels I see at the bar to munch on while we look at the menu?" Zeke said, giving the waitress one of his effortlessly engaging smiles, the one that asked for special service and offered thanks at the same time.

"Sure thing." Bobbie-Sue nodded and hurried away to fill their order.

Ariel hooked a finger over the tortoiseshell nosepiece of her sunglasses and pulled them down at bit. "Friend of yours?" she asked, giving him an arch look over the rim.

Zeke shot her a quick glance across the table, trying to gauge her expression. "Barely an acquaintance," he said, hoping they weren't going to have another discussion about his so-called harem. "I met her for the first time a few days ago at the BA. There's nothing more between us than that."

Ariel smiled to let him know she'd only been teasing. "I wasn't suggesting there was," she said easily, and pushed her sunglasses onto the top of her head.

Ladies' man he might be but she'd never heard anyone accuse him of robbing the cradle—and the waitress was younger than Cameron. She reached out and picked up the narrow, laminated card that stood in the middle of the table. It was shaped like a cocktail shaker, with a list of exotic cocktails and coffee drinks on one side and a menu on the other.

"Here you go." Bobbie-Sue set cocktail napkins, drinks and a small basket of pretzels in front of them. "I don't mean to hurry you," she said, nodding toward the menu Ariel held, "but the kitchen's only open for another twenty minutes." Her smile was bright and apologetic. "You caught us at the tail end of our lunch service."

"Is this the entire menu?" Ariel asked. "Or just the appetizer list?"

"That's it, I'm afraid. I keep telling Eddie—" she motioned toward the bartender with a tilt of her head "—that we should have some crudités or a small salad or something on there. But he said they tried that once and ended up with a kitchen full of wilted lettuce."

"What's the matter with the menu?" Zeke asked, reaching out to pluck it from Ariel's fingers.

"There's nothing on it that isn't deep-fried or covered in sour cream and melted cheese," his ex-wife lamented. "Or both."

"Don't tell me you're worried about a few grams of fat," Zeke teased, giving her an appreciative leer.

"I have to start shooting the new ad campaign for Gavino in two weeks. One of the dresses they want me to wear is short, black and made of Lycra."

"Oh, well, in that case." He put the menu down. "We'll just have the drinks." He looked up at Bobbie-Sue. "And the check."

"The drinks are on me," Bobbie-Sue said, giving him a wide, blindingly sweet smile that positively radiated gratitude and youthful sex appeal. "A small token of my thanks."

Five seconds of ponderous silence descended in her wake. Zeke reached out and picked up his beer, burying his nose in the glass for a long swallow, wondering why he felt so damned guilty all of the sudden. He had nothing to feel guilty about.

Ariel ran her fingertip around the rim of her wine-glass, watching him, wondering if his uneasiness meant he'd taken to robbing cradles, after all, and hating—absolutely hating!—that she felt threatened by a woman young enough to be her daughter.

"A token of her thanks?" she said carefully, when he put his glass down.

"I arranged for her to audition for a bit part in my next movie. She's an actress."

"And?"

"And what?" he snapped, restive and resentful under her accusing gaze. "C'mon, Ariel, give me a break. She's younger than Cameron."

She raised a delicate eyebrow. "I was wondering if you'd noticed that little fact."

"Of course I noticed. Dammit, I'm not some kind of pervert who preys on young—" He stopped and took a deep breath, willing himself to get past the anger. And the hurt. "Look, sweetheart," he said, his tone deliberately even. "I know we have a ways to go on the trust issue here, but could you give me a little credit for basic decency? I don't fool around with women who are young enough to have gone to school with my daughter. And I don't come on to one woman while I'm out with another."

"Then why were you acting so guilty?"

"Because as soon as she smiled at me like that, I knew you were going to start jumping to conclusions."

Ariel sighed and looked down into her drink. He was right. She had jumped to conclusions. He hadn't reacted to the gorgeous young waitress any differently than he did to any of Cameron's friends. He'd been friendly and charming because that's what he was. *She* was the one who'd acted inappropriately by reading more into the situation than was there. She felt like an idiot—a jealous, green-eyed idiot. She hated feeling that way.

"Ariel?"

"I'm sorry," she murmured, still staring down into her drink. "I was out of line. You didn't deserve that." She lifted her gaze without quite lifting her head, looking up at him through a concealing fringe of lashes. "Could we just forget it?" she asked sheepishly.

"It's forgotten." He reached out, covering her hand where it lay on the table, stilling the restless movement of her fingers. "Why don't you drink your wine so we can get out of here and go someplace else for lunch?" he said, giving her fingers a quick, encouraging little squeeze. "There's a restaurant called the Happy Sprout not too far from here."

Ariel turned her hand over, twining her fingers with his when he would have drawn away. "And the Bachelor Arms is right next door, isn't it?" she asked softly.

"Yes," he said, just as softly. "It is." He waited a beat, for whatever she wanted to say next, but she just sat there, staring down at their entwined fingers. "Ariel?"

"We could get something to eat there, couldn't we? You have food in your refrigerator?"

"Yes, of course, but..." He squeezed her fingers again, silently demanding that she look up at him. "Last night you refused to go there with me because of the bad memories."

"I know. But that was last night. And today... well," she sighed. "Today I think it might be time to face some of those memories and try to put them in perspective. I lied when I said they were all bad. They aren't all bad," she admitted, her eyes still lowered, still staring at their clasped hands. "Some of them are very, very good. It's time to face that, too, I think."

"Well, since we're being honest here, I guess I should admit that I lied last night, too," Zeke confessed. "You were right—I had every intention of trying to seduce you if you came to the Bachelor Arms with me." He reached across the table with his free hand and lifted her chin, making her look at him.

Ariel caught her breath, waiting, her gaze riveted to his, knowing there was more by the burning look in his eyes.

"I still intend to," he said, feeling obligated to give her fair warning. "If you'll let me."

Ariel's heart seemed to stop for a second, and then it took up a faster rhythm, slamming against the wall of her chest. "And if I won't?"

"Then we'll just have lunch."

Their gazes held for a second or two longer, blue eyes staring into brown—hesitant, wary, longing.

"I won't do anything you don't want me to do," he said. "And I promise, whatever happens, I'll take it slow. Trust me."

12

THEY ENTERED the Bachelor Arms through the wrought iron gate of the quiet courtyard instead of the lobby, in an effort to avoid running into anyone who might recognize them. But they needn't have bothered. The building was nearly empty, snoozing in the peaceful and placid quiet of midafternoon when the people who lived in it were gone for the day. Ken Amberson was on his knees, weeding an overgrown bed of hibiscus. He looked up as they passed, following them with his pale gray gaze as they made their way across the sunscorched concrete. They didn't glance at each other as they walked down the hall to apartment 1-G. They didn't talk. They didn't even touch.

They didn't have to.

The air between them was charged with electricity, thick and heavy with the anticipation of what might be, seething with memories of what had been before, connecting them as surely as if they had still been holding each other's hands.

Inevitably, they were both remembering the first time they had made love. The same place. The same time of day. The same season of the year. She had been in a quiet panic, both excited and frightened by what was about to happen. He had been uncharacteristically nervous, afraid his eagerness would scare her off before he even got her inside the apartment.

Nothing had changed.

Stopping in front of the door to 1-G, Zeke unlocked it, pushed it open and stepped aside, extending his hand to usher her in ahead of him. For a moment, he was afraid she wouldn't enter, but she took a quick breath and stepped over the threshold.

She didn't know what she had expected. The smell of incense, maybe, underscored by the distinctly sweet scent of marijuana. The pulsing sound of Steppenwolf or Three Dog Night, rolling down the hall. The black light posters of Jimi Hendrix, Janis Joplin and The Grateful Dead that had once decorated the foyer wall. But the apartment was cool and quiet, the air smelled faintly of potpourri and lemon oil, and there was a Georgia O'Keeffe where Jimi Hendrix had been.

Ariel turned around, not sure whether she meant to make some comment about the changes he had made, or bolt out of the apartment. But Zeke had already closed the door, and locked it. He stood there, his Raiders cap held loosely in his hands, his back to the door, watching her as if he knew she was thinking about running. He had her now, and he wasn't about to let her go, his steady look said. Not until they'd come to some kind of deeper understanding.

Ariel turned away without a word and started down the hall. She could feel his gaze on her as he followed, and she shivered, the feeling rippling down her spine as if he had actually reached out and run his finger down her back.

The living room was a curious, unsettling blend of the past and the present. She slipped her sunglasses off, twisting them between her fingers as she looked around the room. The tall arched windows were the same as the first time she had been there; the wooden shutters; the shabby-genteel, old world charm of the place; even the old Victorian pewter mirror on the wall were all the same. But the beaded curtains were gone; there were no lava lamps or garishly colored beanbag chairs; the secondhand sofa and cable-spool coffee table had been replaced by simple Mission furniture and soothing colors that didn't overshadow the natural elegance of the space.

"It's lovely," she murmured, unable to think of anything else to say.

"I'll tell Patsy you said so," Zeke said as he reached out to relieve her of both her tan leather shoulder bag and the sunglasses that dangled, unheeded, from one hand. He set them down on the coffee table in front of the sofa, along with his Raiders cap, and crossed over to the built-in bookcases that housed an impressive array of audio-video equipment and small objets d'art.

Without asking her what she'd like to hear, or taking the time to make a careful selection, he inserted a CD into the player and pushed the On button. He'd played Creedence Clearwater for her last time, she remembered, at decibel levels loud enough to be heard in the next apartment. This time the music was classical, something soft and romantic, just loud enough to be heard under the hum of conversation. If there had been any conversation.

They stood there with the width of the room between them, staring at each other, like two tongue-tied teenagers, each waiting for the other to make the first move.

He wasn't so far removed from the young man he had been, Ariel thought. Standing there, with the soft light from the window at his back, he might almost be the boy she had first fallen in love with. His gleaming sable hair was a little gray at the temples now, his shoulders were heavier, and the shirt tucked into his snug, faded jeans was made of soft expensive white linen instead of tie-dyed cotton. But nothing else seemed to have changed. He still stood in that cocky hip-shot stance, he still exuded raw sex appeal and bad-boy charm, he still made her heart flutter in her chest like a wild bird.

Zeke couldn't believe she was finally here, in the apartment where it had all started, standing in almost the same place she had stood before. She was wearing pale apple green this time, instead of daffodil yellow, a deceptively simple sheath of a dress in a slightly nubby fabric, sleeveless, with the collar turned up against the back of her neck and a row of tiny wooden buttons running all the way down the front to the gently flaring, calf-length hem. Her pale gold hair was cut in a simple sophisticated style that fell to her shoulders from an off-center part instead of cascading down her back like a silken waterfall. But she still looked as fresh and innocent as springtime. And she still had that same startled doe look in her big blue eyes.

She was twenty-five years older now, he marveled, a woman instead of a girl, but that look was exactly the same. And he was an experienced man instead of a cocky boy, but it affected him exactly the same way. He crossed the room toward her.

"Why don't we see what's in the refrigerator?" he said, snagging her around the waist as he headed for the kitchen. "I know there's fresh fruit and yogurt, at least."

But this time, instead of letting him propel her along in his wake, Ariel hung back. "I'm not really hungry, after all," she said. The truth was, she didn't think she'd be able to force even a single bite of food past the tightness in her throat. She was too nervous to eat.

"Would you like some wine? Or some mineral water?"

"No."

He shifted his hold on her, turning their bodies so that they stood face-to-face with his arms around her and his hands clasped loosely at the small of her back. "How about a Coke?" he suggested softly, remembering the first time and what they had—or, rather, *hadn't*—had to drink.

Ariel shook her head.

"No lunch," he said lightly, rocking her from side to side in his hold. "Nothing to drink." He touched his forehead to hers. "Does that mean it's all right if I try to seduce you now?" he whispered.

Unconsciously, Ariel's tongue snaked out, moistening her bottom lip. She hadn't expected quite so direct an approach and it left her speechless. "Ah ..."

"Ah?" He pulled back and smiled at her, the look in his eyes wicked and tender at the same time. "Is that a yes or a no?"

Ariel opened her mouth to answer him, but the words wouldn't come. To answer in the affirmative would be to make herself vulnerable again, to admit that she wanted—*needed*—what only he could give her. She didn't want to need him. But to say no would be a bald-faced lie—one she couldn't bring herself to utter.

She lifted her gaze to his, instead, silently offering what she was too afraid to put into words, hoping he would simply understand and take it. Take her. If she didn't say the words, if she didn't admit to her intemperate, unreasoning need for him, then maybe it wouldn't be quite real. Maybe she could pretend that she wasn't on the verge of committing herself—once again—to a man she didn't trust.

"We could sit on the couch and neck like we did the last time. Remember?" He bent his head, nuzzling aside her collar to press a soft kiss on the side of her throat. "You were so sweet, and so scared."

Ariel managed to shake her head at that, but gently so as not to halt the gentle exploration of his lips along her throat.

"Are you scared now?" he murmured.

"No," she said, but it was a lie, just like the last time. She was terrified. More now than before, because now she knew how much he could hurt her. The thought made her tremble.

Zeke lifted his head to look at her. "Have you changed your mind, sweetheart? Would you like to just have lunch, after all?"

"No," she said to his throat.

"Then would you look at me, please?"

Slowly, she lifted her head and looked at him. Her eyes were wide and blue and wondering, just like the last time. And he could see the fear there, too, also like the last time. But underneath... thank God, underneath there was sweet feminine heat, and the banked, burning desires of a woman, not a girl.

Zeke smiled. "Shall we start in here on the couch like we did before, or go straight to the bedroom? Tell me," he coaxed when she blushed and remained silent. "I want to know what you want. I want to know *everything* you want." He brushed his lips across hers. "Tell me."

With an inarticulate cry, Ariel went up on her toes and wrapped her arms around his neck, pulling his head down to hers, stopping the tantalizing flow of words.

There was a searing flash of heat as their mouths met, a fierce, fervent surge of blood that drowned all coherent thought in a tempestuous rush of sensation. Zeke crushed her in his arms, dragging her closer, tighter, forgetting, for the moment, that he meant to seduce and not ravage.

Yes, she thought, as she yielded herself to him. *Yes*, this was what she wanted. Needed. To be swept away, and swept along in the firestorm of his passion the way she had been last night, with no time to think or consider. She felt herself lifted up off the floor and she grasped him tighter, holding on, pressing desperate kisses to his jaw and throat as he carried her down the hall to the bedroom.

She caught a quick glimpse of their reflection in the old Victorian mirror as they passed it; a fleeting image of herself being swept away in Zeke's strong arms as he strode toward the bedroom. There was something else in the mirror, too, a flash of white, a flicker of something . . . or someone . . . but Ariel forgot all about it as Zeke turned sideways and shouldered open the bedroom door.

Yes, she exalted, as he laid her down on the bed. *Yes*, this was *exactly* what she wanted. To be overwhelmed. Overpowered. Taken.

But he wasn't cooperating.

"Ariel," he murmured raggedly, resisting the pull of her arms when she would have dragged him down on top of her. "Sweetheart, wait a minute. Please." He grasped her hands in his, pulling them away from his shoulders, pushing them down to the bed on either side of her head.

She moaned in distress and squirmed against him, trying to wriggle her hands out from under his.

"Ariel, sweetheart." He half groaned, half laughed, the sound breathless and rough and excited. "I thought you wanted to slow things down."

"Not this," she murmured, and arched against him so that her breasts grazed his chest.

Even through their layers of clothing, the contact was electric. Zeke moaned but sat up, managing to resist her siren's call. "Well, *I* want to take things slow. Slow is better sometimes," he said raggedly. "And I promised, remember?" He lifted one of the hands he held captive, bringing it to his lips. "Let me show you that you can trust me, sweetheart. Let me keep my promise."

He kissed her clenched fingers, nuzzling his lips against them until they opened. And then he kissed her palm, softly, and brushed his lips lightly back and forth over the scented, sensitive skin of her wrist, and then further, planting whisper soft kisses along the length of her arm to the pale, fragile skin at the crook of her elbow.

He heard her sigh, felt the tension in her begin to relax under his gentle, undemanding touch. The hand still beneath his on the bed opened under his urging, the slender fingers spreading to twine with his. She murmured, drugged with the sweet pleasure of his soft caresses, and turned her head on the pillow, arching her neck, offering it as his lips journeyed up her shoulder.

Yes, he thought, as he folded back the collar of her dress to feast on her throat. This was the way it should be. This sweet surrender, this soft, slow arousal of the senses. He wanted to evoke that first time all over again, when it had been nothing but good between them. And then he wanted to make it better. To bind her to him with the strong, silken bonds of pleasure and voluptuous satisfaction. To make her yearn for him the way he yearned for her. To make her ache with the same heated, helpless desire he felt every time he looked at her. He hadn't known how to do that twenty-five years ago, he hadn't had the patience or the skill, or the knowledge to do it. Now, he had all three and he meant to use them to his advantage. And hers.

He undressed her slowly, tenderly, pausing often for soft kisses and soothing, gentle caresses, murmuring breathless accolades to her beauty, touching her lightly, skillfully, holding himself back until she was hot and soft and utterly defenseless under his hands.

Ariel had thought she'd remembered what it was like to be loved by Zeke. The trembling excitement of it, the breathless pleasure, the flash and fire...but where had this mindless helplessness come from? This languid softness inside herself? She felt as if she were drifting, floating through a heated cloud, buoyed by the gentle brush of his hands on her skin. Her body was pliant to his slightest touch, her will nonexistent, her mind fogged with pleasure. She found herself naked without quite knowing how it had happened. And then he was naked, too, his body stretched out beside hers, long and hard and hot. The clouds in her mind parted, just a little, and the unfocused sensations of pleasure sharpened.

His lips skimmed down the center of her chest to pluck delicately at her nipples. His tongue laved them, caressing them to turgid life. The hand gently stroking the curve of her waist and hip slid around to knead the fleshy globe of her bottom. His hard, hair-roughened thigh slipped between hers, pressing up against the moist heated core of her desire. His erection rubbed insistently against the sensitive crease between her hip and the top of her thigh.

A bit more of Ariel's languor vanished. She sighed and lifted her arms to wrap them around him, silently demanding more. More kisses. Deeper caresses. More. She smoothed her hands over the hard curve of his biceps and up over his shoulder and down the long, strong muscles of his back, feeling them flex and bunch beneath her palms. She caressed the nape of his neck, curling her fingers into his dark, shaggy hair to hold him as he suckled her. *More,* she thought. *I want more.*

But the silent demands weren't frantic or hurried. Enough of the clouds remained to soften the harsh edges of desire, and she knew, instinctively, he would give her what she craved. What she needed. All she had to do was wait. Accept. Receive. Absorb.

She kept her hands in his hair as he moved his head down her body. Not directing or guiding his movement, but caressing only, her palms curved around the shape of his head, her fingers stroking lightly, needing to give back some of the tenderness he was giving her. Her thighs opened for him easily, soft and fluid as water, and she sighed when he parted her petaled folds with gentle fingertips and began to love her with his mouth.

The breathy sigh turned to a low moan, and then a gasp when the first small explosion of heat rolled through her. Her fingers tightened in his hair; her back lifted from the bed; the muscles in her stomach and long smooth thighs tensed. He let the tension recede—turning his head to brush his lips against the inside of each quivering thigh to soothe her—and then drove her up again, a little faster, a little higher, a little hotter. She moaned again, a plaintive sound of need and desire, and tugged on his hair. There was a shifting of bodies, a rearranging of limbs. And then he slipped into her, easily, perfectly.

Yes! The word could have been a murmur, or a sigh, or merely a shared thought as they lay very still, savoring the transcendent, sumptuous melding of their flesh.

And then, slowly, prodded by the steadily increasing heat, they roused themselves, answering the age-old call to mate. His movements within her were steady and strong, slow-burning this time, like the embers of a fire rather than the crackling, fast-burning flame. Her pelvis rolled up to meet each heavy, measured thrust of his hips, taking him deep, and then deeper, each time. She felt as if her body were a furnace, glowing red, molten, growing hotter and hotter with each slow, deliberate stroke. And then finally... finally... the last of the languor vanished altogether. The molten ember that was her body burst into a white-hot flame, pulsating, throbbing with exquisite feeling. With a low, voluptuous groan of utter satisfaction, Ariel arched her back and gave herself up to the heat. And to him.

"I love you," he whispered, as the fire took him.

Ariel held him tight and let herself believe it.

THEY FOUND FRUIT in Zeke's refrigerator, and smoked salmon and three kinds of cheese. A quick search of the cupboards yielded whole wheat crackers, a small round loaf of pumpernickel bread and a bag of Pepperidge Farm Milano Mint cookies. "A feast," Ariel said, as she arranged everything on a tray for him to carry into the living room.

They sat facing each other at opposite ends of the wide, cushy sofa, their feet stretched out, bare soles touching. Zeke wore his jeans and the slanting rays of sunlight streaming in through the open windows. Ariel had wrapped herself in the thick blue terry robe she'd found hanging on the back of the bathroom door. Zeke thought it made her eyes glow like sapphires.

"How did you end up here?" Ariel asked, gesturing at the room with the cookie she held in her fingers. "It's a surprisingly lovely apartment, given the location and everything, but somehow I don't quite see it as you. Not even for six weeks or so. I would have expected you just to get a suite at the Regent Beverly Wilshire or rent one of the bungalows at the Beverly Hills Hotel." *Or bunk in with one of your women.* The thought skipped through her mind—fleetingly—but she resolutely pushed it away. She was feeling too relaxed. Too mellow. Too...loved. And she didn't want anything to spoil the mood. "Why here?"

"I'm beginning to think it was fate."

"Fate?" She washed a bite of cookie down with a sip of mineral water. "How so?"

"I was actually on my way over to the Regent but—what with traffic the way it is and all the construction going on—I had to make a couple of detours. I was turning around in a driveway across the street when I looked up and saw the Bachelor Arms in my rearview mirror." He paused dramatically, instinctively, like the fine actor he was, to let the tension build. "The superintendent was right outside the courtyard, putting up an Apartment For Rent sign. The very same superintendent who was here twenty-five years ago."

"Coincidences happen every day."

"Maybe. Except there's more."

Ariel raised an eyebrow, inviting him to elaborate as she reached for another cookie.

"Do you remember Jack Shannon? Eric Shannon's younger brother?"

"Vaguely. I only met him once or twice—and so much else was going on back then. He was younger than the rest of you, wasn't he? Closer to my age, I think." Her forehead puckered as she tried to recall some elusive bit of information about Jack Shannon. "He was a writer, wasn't he?"

"Reporter," Zeke amended. "He's a married man now, covers the city beat for the *Times*." He gave her a slanted look, knowing how she would take his next words. "His wife's the same age as Cameron."

Ariel's expressive eyes narrowed with disapproval. "You're kidding."

"It's not what you're thinking," Zeke chided gently. "Well, it is, in a way, I guess but..." He shrugged. "You'd have to see them together to understand. They've both been kind of battered by life. She's a lot wiser than her years and, in a strange way, he's younger than his. They're good together," he said, unable to explain it any better. "You'll have to read Jack's screenplay to really understand about them. It's on the desk in my office." He grinned. "His wife sent it to me by special messenger."

"He's a screenwriter, too?"

Zeke nodded. "I've already told him I want to produce *Lovers and Strangers*. And I want the right of first refusal on anything else he writes."

"He's that good?"

Zeke nodded again. "And that's not all." He waited until she raised an impatient eyebrow at him. "He was also apartment 1-G's previous tenant. He and Faith— that's his wife's name—were moving out the day I stopped by to look at the place."

Ariel paused with her bottle of mineral water half-way to her mouth. "You mean he'd been living here all this time? In the building where his brother died? That's macabre."

"No," Zeke said. "He'd only been living here for a couple of months. He said he'd been—and I quote—'drawn back' to the place."

Ariel shivered in the warm room. "Because of his brother's death?"

"Partly. He said he'd never really come to grips with Eric's suicide and the reasons for it, so there were a lot of issues to resolve. He felt he had to come back here to resolve them."

"And did he?"

"He's made his peace with it." Zeke sat up and reached toward the tray on the coffee table, helping himself to a serving of smoked salmon and cream cheese on pumpernickel. "And he and Faith are very happy," he said, and popped the morsel into his mouth. "He's convinced that she was the main reason he was drawn back. Want one?"

"No, thanks." Ariel waved away his offer. "Why did he think his wife had a part in drawing him back? Was she involved in Eric's suicide somehow?"

"Hardly. Remember, she wasn't even born when Eric committed suicide. Jack met her right here in the Bachelor Arms, less than two months ago." He slanted a glance at her. "And that's where it gets really strange."

"Strange how?"

Zeke grinned and hummed a few bars of the theme from the *Twilight Zone*.

"Stop that," Ariel demanded, nudging his hip with her bare foot. "And tell me what you mean."

"Fate," Zeke said, grasping her foot in his hand to still it. "Destiny. Kismet." He stopped his teasing litany, suddenly remembering . . . *Maybe it's your turn now,* Jack had said to him. And then Natasha Kuryan . . . *You were meant to come back.* Ken Amberson's ramblings about the woman in the mirror and her power to see into the future. Faith Shannon's assertions that the ghost was very real, indeed. Was it possible?

"Zeke?" Ariel sat up, unconsciously scooting closer to him on the sofa. She felt uneasy, suddenly. Edgy and restive without knowing why. "Don't go spooky on me."

"Oh, it's nothing, sweetheart." Deliberately, he shook his strange mood off and reached out, putting an arm around her shoulders to hug her close. "I was just teasing you," he said, and pressed a kiss on top of her head.

"Tell me," she demanded.

"It's just a sad, silly story about some poor girl who drowned in the swimming pool that used to be down in the courtyard. Somehow, it's achieved legend status over the years."

"So tell me," she said again. "I like a good ghost story as well as the next person."

So Zeke told her about the young woman who had died under mysterious circumstances, about the legend that had grown up around the same time about the appearances of a ghostly woman in the old mirror in 1-G and her alleged ability to herald boon or bane to those who were lucky—or unlucky—enough to see her.

"I think old Amberson's the one who keeps the legend alive," Zeke said, giving her shoulders a little squeeze before he let them go. "He's never seen her himself, of course, but apparently, he tells the story to everyone who moves in here. He's a strange old bird. Do you want any more of this?" he asked, gesturing at the tray.

Ariel shook her head, watching as he picked it up and carried it into the kitchen. And then, when he was no longer in sight, her gaze wandered, inevitably, over to the mirror.

Had she seen something there when he carried her to bed? Someone? And if she had, was that someone trying to tell her that believing in Zeke's love would make all her dreams come true? Or warn her that her ex-husband was about to break her heart again?

13

"LAST CHANCE to change your mind," Zeke whispered, bending his head so that only his daughter could hear him. "If we leave now no one would even notice until it was too late to stop us. I could have you halfway to Mexico before—"

Cameron jabbed him in the ribs with her elbow. "Oh, Dad," she said, trying not to giggle and spoil the solemnity of the moment. "Behave."

"What?" he demanded in a deliberately injured tone, rubbing his side as if she had really hurt him. "What did I say? I was only trying to help you out of this mess you've gotten yourself into."

Cameron turned her head, giving him a knowing look through the misty tulle of her veil. "I know what you're trying to do." She tilted her head, touching her temple to his shoulder for just a moment in one of her typical gestures of affection. "And I love you for it, Daddy."

Zeke felt a lump the size of a baseball form in his throat. His daughter was getting married. His baby girl. He'd been talking nonstop nonsense to her all the way over to the church, giving her something to think about besides the butterflies he knew were fluttering around beneath the Chantilly lace of her tight-waisted wedding gown.

Now, suddenly, he couldn't have uttered another word to save his life. His *baby* was getting married!

"It's almost time," Leslie Fine said. She moved around behind them, making small adjustments to Cameron's already perfectly arranged train, tweaking the side of her veil into even more perfect folds around her shining blond head. "Wait just another moment and..." The five-note trumpet herald faded into silence and the first strains of the "Wedding March" swelled through the church. "Now," she said and touched Zeke's shoulder to get him started.

He couldn't seem to make his feet move.

"It's okay, Dad," Cameron whispered, patting his arm with the hand she had linked through his elbow. "There's nothing to be nervous about."

Zeke looked down to find his daughter smiling up at him through the gossamer sheerness of her veil, her face as calm and serene as the Madonna's, her dark eyes glowing with happiness, her nervousness miraculously gone now that they were finally ready to start.

"I love you, baby," Zeke murmured, forcing the words through the lump in his throat. And then, covering the cool, slender fingers that lay on his sleeve with the warmth of his hand, he started his daughter down the aisle toward her future.

His mind was all on Cameron as they paced slowly down the center aisle of the church. Pictures of her as she had been at different stages of her life kaleidoscoped through his mind in rapid succession. He remembered the sunshine brilliance of her wide, toothless baby grin and the way she used to raise her arms, demanding to be picked up whenever she saw him. He remembered the determined way she would toddle after him whenever he brought her on the set, ignoring the blandishments of the cast and crew in favor of being her father's faithful shadow. He remembered the way she'd always come flying into his arms whenever he picked her up from school, eager to show him her latest drawing or the A she'd got on her spelling test. He remembered, too, the way she had always come running to her daddy to make it better, whether it was a skinned knee or a project gone wrong or a thoughtless boy who'd broken her heart.

She wouldn't be turning to him first anymore to soothe her hurts and share her joys, but to the young man waiting for her at the front of the church. And that was as it should be, Zeke knew. It was the way he'd always hoped it would be for her. Still, he found himself blinking back tears as they reached the front of the church and the moment came for him to give his daughter's hand into the keeping of the young man who was now first in her loving heart.

In a gesture that was unconsciously theatrical, instinctively gallant and completely heartfelt, he raised Cameron's hand to his lips and pressed a kiss to the back of her slender fingers. "Be happy, baby," he said, and relinquished her to her future husband.

Sitting in the front pew, watching the tender exchange of feeling between her ex-husband and her only child, Ariel pressed her lips together and tried hard to keep from crying. She'd promised herself she wouldn't cry. A wedding was a joyous occasion, a celebration of two people in love pledging themselves to each other for all time.

Except that her wedding hadn't been that way at all. Ariel clenched her hands together in her lap. No, she wouldn't think of that now. She'd promised herself she wouldn't let the sad memories of her own wedding intrude on the happiness she felt at seeing her daughter exchange vows with the man of her choice.

But the memories were there, painful memories of another young man in a rented tuxedo standing, distant and rigid, by her side as she pledged her eternal love. Of a kiss that was as cold as death. Of a smile that never reached his eyes. She'd carried off her part in the joyless charade with cool professionalism, her acting skills equal to her groom's in every way as she presented the happy, smiling facade expected of America's sweetheart on her wedding day. And then she'd spent her wedding night alone, in a storm of bitter weeping.

She looked up as Zeke slid into the pew next to her, her wide blue eyes made crystalline by the sheen of unshed tears, unsure, just then, of who they were for.

"I know," Zeke murmured, reaching out to cover her hands where they lay clenched together in the lap of her pale pink silk dress. "I know, sweetheart."

Ariel smiled tremulously and unclenched her fingers, twining them with his, holding his big warm hand between both of hers. It didn't matter, suddenly, if his sympathetic murmur had been in response to past pain or present joy. It only mattered that he was there. That he cared. That he was sitting beside her with his hand in hers while their daughter pledged herself in marriage. It made her think that maybe, just maybe, everything would turn out all right.

THE RECEPTION was lavish and grand, warm and festive, elegant and fun. They had a champagne brunch for three hundred guests under white silk tents set up on the sweeping lawn. There were silly toasts and serious, heartfelt speeches. The best man got a little drunk and made a pass at the maid of honor and one of the caterer's assistants. The four-year-old flower girl wet her pants and had to be taken upstairs and set to rights. The groom's parents demonstrated the proper way to dance the hully-gully. And the bride's paternal grandmother from New York spent most of her time flirting with one of the guests, a handsome and legendary movie star who flirted right back.

"It was a lovely wedding," said a soft voice at Zeke's elbow. "And a great reception. Ariel always has been the perfect hostess."

"Yes, she has," Zeke said, turning away from the activity on the terrace cum dance floor to smile at his second ex-wife, Holly Neals. She was tall and blade slender, with sleek platinum blond hair worn in a sophisticated wedge, a disarmingly sweet smile and a killer intellect. Which was why, fifteen years after their divorce, she was still his lawyer. "Hello, Holly," he said genially, leaning down to kiss her cheek. "I missed you in the receiving line."

"I sneaked in during brunch. I had to stop by my office on the way over from the church."

"On a Saturday?"

"The wheels of justice just keep on turning," Holly said with a shrug.

"You're obsessed with your work," Zeke countered, and then grinned. "Which is just part of what makes you such a damned good lawyer."

"Mmm," Holly murmured absently. "Speaking of obsessions . . ." She tucked her flat envelope handbag under her arm and reached up, using both hands to straighten his satin bow tie. "I've seen those scorching looks you've been aiming at the mother of our blushing bride." She patted the tie into place. "Any new developments there or is it just the usual unrequited passion?"

Her voice was just a little sharp, a little pointed, even after fifteen years. Zeke's obsession with his first wife was one of the main reasons Holly had declined to remain his second. In the beginning she hadn't known *whom* she was being compared to, but she knew damn well she was being compared—and falling woefully short. It had made their brief two-year marriage a volatile one, straining the friendship that had led them to take the unwise step into wedded bliss in the first place. In the end, they'd both agreed they made better friends than lovers. The split had been exceedingly amicable but, sometimes, when the opportunity presented itself, Holly couldn't quite resist the urge to needle him for finding her less than perfect.

"Ariel and I are in the process of, ah...reassessing our relationship," Zeke said carefully.

"Reassessing?" Holly tilted her head, sending a sheaf of platinum hair over one eye as she considered him. "That's a new word for it."

"But an accurate one. We're—"

She lost his attention as he caught sight of someone outside her line of vision. The expression in his dark eyes told her who it was without her having to turn her head to look. Ariel Cameron. America's sweetheart. Ms. Perfect. Holly sighed. Just once before she died, she wished some man would look at her the way Zeke was looking at Ariel, with his whole heart in his eyes.

"Don't sign any prenuptial agreement without letting me read it first," she said wryly, effectively bringing his attention back to her.

"Prenuptial...?" he began, but she stopped his denials with a fingertip to his lips.

"I really hope it works out for you this time," she said, meaning it sincerely. "You've always loved her."

Zeke smiled and reached up, pressing her fingertips
to his lips for a quick, friendly kiss before drawing them
down to hold them in his. "Yes, I have," he admitted.
"I wonder why you knew that before I did?"

"Because you're a thickheaded, unevolved male,
that's why," she said with a teasing grin. "And I'm
a—"

She'd lost him again; he was looking past her, a faint
worried frown between his eyes.

"I have to go find Cameron and give her a kiss before I leave," Holly said, and pulled her hand out of his.

That brought his attention back to her. For a moment. "You're not staying?" His gaze flickered past her
shoulder again, just briefly, before he remembered his
manners and brought it back to her face. "Cameron's
supposed to throw the bouquet in a few minutes."

"I wish I could stay for that," she said, "but I have a
stack of depositions to read before Monday."

"Well, take care, then." He leaned down and pressed
a quick, absent kiss on her lips. "I'll call you next week
about that real estate deal in the Valley," he said, already striding past her before the last words were out
of his mouth.

He threaded his way through the crowd on the dance
floor, unerringly following the path taken by his first
ex-wife. "Ariel," he murmured, reaching out to grasp
her arm and claim her attention.

She turned around at his touch, regal, remote, icily
polite. "Yes?"

Zeke felt his gut tighten. "I know what you're thinking," he said, low, aware of the wedding guests all
around them, "but you've got it all wrong."

"No," she said, her voice well-modulated and perfectly pleasant—in case anyone was listening. "I've just realized I had it right all along."

"Ariel, dammit—"

She froze him with a glance. "Cameron's going upstairs to change into her going away outfit before she throws the bouquet," she said, looking pointedly down at the hand still on her arm. "She's expecting me to help her."

"All right." Zeke took a deep, calming breath. "All right. You go on upstairs and help Cameron change. We'll talk about this when everyone's gone."

"We'll talk about it when hell freezes over," Ariel snapped and jerked her arm out of his hand, for once completely forgetting her image.

CAMERON PAUSED at the top of the wide, sweeping staircase, her slender figure clad in a pale rose-and-cream French challis dress, her face wreathed in smiles, her arm teasingly poised to throw the bouquet. Her mother stood behind her, up on the wide landing, her blue eyes misty with pride and love. Her father stood by the open front door, back behind the shuffling, giggling group of women and girls gathered in the grand foyer for a chance to catch the bridal trophy. Her new husband, dressed in tan chinos and a navy sport coat, waited at the foot of the stairs.

"Ready?" Cameron called merrily, and then cocked her arm and threw the bouquet.

She was halfway down the stairs before it was caught by one of her bridesmaids, already safe in the circle of her husband's arm as they raced for the front door. Zeke went with them to the limo, running interference through the throng of laughing, rice-throwing wedding guests. There was a flurry of goodbyes and congratulations and then Cameron went up on tiptoe to kiss her father goodbye.

"I was really hoping you and Mom had come to some sort of new understanding during this last week," she said, drawing back to stare into his eyes. "But upstairs just now her attitude toward you was..." Cameron shrugged uncertainly.

Zeke hugged his daughter tight. "Don't you worry about your mother and me," he said, and drew back to kiss her cheek again before assisting her into the limousine. "We'll come to a new understanding on our own. I promise."

MOST OF THE WEDDING guests lingered another hour or so, happily rehashing the wedding and drinking up the last of the champagne. The catering staff and cleanup crew were underfoot for another two hours after that. And the relatives who'd flown in from New York had to be transported back to their suite of rooms at the Regent Beverly Wilshire. Zeke saw to that personally, finally settling the last of them into one of the waiting limos fifteen minutes after the cleaning crew had slammed the rear doors on their van and disappeared down the long curving driveway.

The wedding was over.

The reception was over.

The new Mr. and Mrs. Everett were safely away, winging over the blue Pacific to the island of Maui.

Eleanor had retired to her apartment over the garage to put her feet up.

And Ariel was nowhere to be seen.

Zeke sighed wearily, absently reaching up to loosen his bow tie as he headed up the wide brick steps to the front door. It was locked. Stunned, Zeke looked down, jiggling the ornate brass handle again just to make sure. Definitely locked. Suddenly, the anger he had been holding in since Ariel had pinned him with that cool, accusing stare of hers bubbled to the surface like a geyser.

Damn her!

She was hiding again. Running away. Refusing to let him explain. Refusing, damn it, to trust him.

This time she wasn't getting away with it!

In a tearing rage, Zeke tramped around the side of the big, sprawling house, past the detached garage and the tennis court to the pool at the back. The kitchen door was locked, too, and the wide French doors that opened from the sunroom. Not about to be denied, Zeke turned and mounted the brick steps that led up to the narrow veranda on the second floor. He could see into her bedroom through the multipaned glass doors; the white wall-to-wall carpet, the big white satin-covered bed, the flowing white drapes. The only color in the room came from the pale pink silk dress draped across the white velvet bench at the foot of the bed and the matching high-heeled lizard pumps lying on the floor beside it. Zeke lifted his hand and rapped sharply on the glass door.

Silence.

He rapped again, then dropped his hand and rattled the door knob. "Dammit, Ariel, I know you're in there," he shouted. "Now, open the damn door!"

She appeared, suddenly, from another room, clutching the satin lapels of a white cashmere robe together over her chest. Her feet were bare and there was a narrow white band around her head, the kind a woman wore to hold back her hair while she washed her face. She looked as beautiful as a princess and as cold as ice. "Go away," she shouted, staring at him mulishly through the glass.

"Open the door, Ariel."

"We have nothing to say to each other."

"Open the door, dammit, or I'll kick it in."

She clutched her robe tighter to her chest, a reaction to the shiver that suddenly raced through her body. "You wouldn't."

"You think not?" He drew back as if preparing to do exactly what he'd threatened.

"I've already set the alarm. It will go off. The police will come." She took a step toward the door, her hand out as if to ward him off. "Zeke, no! The tabloids will have a field day if you do it."

"Then open the damn door!"

Ariel hesitated for a moment, then dropped her hand and stepped back. "No," she said, and stood watching him through the glass, her head up, waiting to see what he would do. Would he accept defeat again? Would he turn and walk away again, leaving her to doubt and cry and die inside? "I won't open the door," she said, goading him.

"Then you'd better get ready to see pictures of yourself in your nightclothes smeared all over the front pages." He lifted his foot and kicked in the door.

Wood splintered. Glass tinkled. But no alarm went off.

They stood there, staring at each other across the ruined threshold of the open door. Zeke was tall and dark and suddenly dangerous, the power in his broad shoulders barely constrained by the elegance of his tuxedo jacket, his bow tie undone and dangling down the pristine front of his white silk shirt. Ariel was small and delicate, vulnerable in her bare feet and naked face, her slender body outlined beneath the clinging folds of the white robe. Ten seconds passed, then twenty, and still they stared, their eyes intense and focused, their breath coming fast and shallow, their blood pounding through their veins.

There was challenge in the air—the most basic kind of man-woman challenge. And sex—raw, unadulterated sex at its most fundamental level. The air vibrated with it, stretching nerves and tempers tight.

Zeke stepped into her bedroom, crushing broken glass under the soles of his shoes. "You were bluffing about the alarm," he said as he moved across the carpet toward her. His expression was intent and menacing. His hot, dark eyes never left her face, silently telegraphing his instinctive determination to master her. "Why?"

Ariel stood her ground, haughty as a queen, refusing to quail before his intimidating male swagger. "I didn't think you'd dare."

Zeke reached out and wrapped his hand around the back of her head, cupping it, drawing her to him. "Don't you know I'd dare anything for you?"

She put her hands on his chest, holding him off. "You didn't before."

He didn't pretend not to know what she meant. "I was a boy before. A callow boy who wasn't nearly as smart or as tough as he thought he was. I didn't have the sense or the guts to fight for what was already mine."

"I'm not yours," she said, just to hear him refute it.

"Don't lie," he ordered roughly. "You've been mine since the day we met." He fisted his hand in her hair, drawing her head farther back, dislodging the narrow white headband. It fell to the floor unheeded. "Admit it. You've always been mine."

She stared up at him in mute refusal.

"I'll make you admit it," he vowed and crushed his mouth to hers.

The kiss was hot, lush and intemperate, as all-consuming as a forest fire raging over dry brush. Both of them were breathless when he finally lifted his head. Both of them were shaking with need.

"This isn't going to solve anything," Ariel murmured as he bent and lifted her into his arms.

"The hell it isn't," he growled, and dumped her on the bed.

She put her hands out as he followed her down onto the satin coverlet, spreading her fingers wide against the fine white silk shirt that covered his heaving chest. She could feel his heart slamming against her palms, and her own heart pounded wildly in answer. It would be so easy to just give in to the passion he roused in her. So easy to let him give her what her quivering body so desperately wanted. So easy…and so wrong. For both of them.

"Please, Zeke," she whispered raggedly. "We have to talk."

He hesitated for a long moment, staring down at her, knowing he could overcome her resistance, knowing she wanted him as much as he wanted her. If he lowered himself onto her, those pale slender hands would slide up his chest and around his neck, those soft lips would open, those long slender thighs would part in welcome and surrender. Just the way they always had whenever he'd gotten close enough to touch her like this.

"Please," she murmured. "Don't."

Zeke uttered a low, frustrated growl and levered himself to his feet. "All right, fine. We'll talk." He turned away, pacing to the open door. "But I won't apologize again," he said, staring out into the gathering twilight. "I'm tired of being made to feel guilty for something I didn't do. And for things I haven't even thought of doing." He turned around to face her. "There's nothing between Holly and me except friendship and a warm professional relationship. I share the same kind of relationship with any number of other women but, dammit, I'm not the Casanova the tabloids make me out to be. I like women. I enjoy their company and the way their minds work and their perspective on the world. I always have. It's not something I'm going to apologize or feel guilty for."

"I haven't asked you to apologize for anything."

"Haven't you?"

"No, I haven't. I just . . ." Ariel hesitated, unsure of what to say, how to say it. He'd gotten her so rattled, so confused, wrecking havoc with her emotions and cracking her control. He always had. She put her hand to her forehead and closed her eyes, trying to think, trying to regain her detachment by shutting him out for a moment, trying to gather her thoughts and reestablish some semblance of control over herself.

"Dammit, Ariel, don't do that!" he shouted.

Her eyes flew open.

"Don't shut me out. Not now. Not again."

"Shut you out?" she murmured, puzzled.

"I let you get away with it once. Hell, I let you get away with it for twenty-five years! But that's over. No more America's sweetheart, do you understand me?" He crossed the room again, grasping her by the upper arms before she could think to move away. "It's just you

and me, right here, right now. A man and a woman."
He gave her a little shake. "So deal with it."

"I don't know what you're talking about."

"The hell you don't." He flung her away from him so
forcefully that she almost fell back against the bed. "You
use your image like a shield to keep people from getting too close. Hell—" he paced to the open door and
back again "—you use it like a damn weapon. Ariel
Cameron, America's perfect little girl, all grown up into
the perfect little lady. A cool, cheery little Stepford wife.
Impeccable manners. Unshakable calm. Nothing gets
to her. Tell me," he said, crowding her back against the
edge of the bed, instinctively trying to intimidate her
with his greater size and strength, "doesn't it get tiring,
keeping up the facade, day after day, year after year?
Don't you ever long to let the real you out once in a
while? To say, 'The hell with it. This is who I am, take
it or leave it'?"

Ariel clenched her hands at her sides, fighting the
urge to do just that. "It's not a facade," she insisted. "It's
who am."

"No." He reached out and, very gently, touched the
soft, velvety skin of her flushed cheek. "*This* is is who
you are. This vibrant, passionate woman who—"

"No." Ariel shook her head, clenching her hands
tighter, leaving imprints of her nails in her soft palms.
"No, it's not," she said vehemently.

Too vehemently.

Zeke frowned and took a half step back to look at
her. *Really* look at her. She was rigid, her hands
clenched at her sides, her face pale, her eyes wide. Puzzled realization dawned. "What are you so afraid of?"
he murmured.

She dropped her gaze, quickly, protectively, and tried to back away but the bed blocked her movement. "I'm not afraid of anything," she insisted, but the tone was weak and unconvincing.

"Yes, you are. You're terrified." He put his hand under her chin, gently forcing it up. "Of what?"

Ariel kept her gaze lowered, refusing to look at him, refusing to answer.

"What are you afraid of, Ariel?" he persisted. "Me?"

She lifted her gaze, then, her eyes cool and disdainful, haughty as an outraged queen. "Don't flatter yourself."

"Of what, then?" he prodded relentlessly. "Yourself?"

She exploded into action, slapping his hand away as if it burned her skin. "All right, yes!" she spat, suddenly all fire and fury. The outraged ice queen was gone; a flaming virago had taken her place. "Yes, I'm afraid of myself. Does that satisfy you? Does that make you happy? I'm afraid of myself and what happens when I let my emotions take over and I lose control. I'm afraid of— No—" She twisted away from him when he would have reached for her again. "Don't touch me." She came up against her dressing table. "I don't want you to touch me."

"I have to."

"I said *no*," she shouted and reached behind her, fumbling for something to throw. She came up with a silver-lidded crystal powder box. "Stay away from me."

Zeke shook his head and kept coming.

Ariel cocked her arm and let fly, fully intending to brain him. The heavy crystal box missed his head but hit his shoulder, sending a shower of expensive face powder down the front of his custom-tailored tuxedo.

"Oh, now see what you made me do!" she wailed, horrified by her behavior.

He caught her wrist and there was a brief, unequal struggle before Ariel collapsed, sobbing, into his arms. He gathered her close, trying to soothe and comfort her—and valiantly ignored the fact that he was more turned on than he had ever been in his life. Who'd have thought his Ariel, his sweet, cool perfect Ariel, would have the temper of a shrew?

"Sweetheart, don't," he murmured. "Don't cry. It's all right."

"It's not all right!" she said and tried to push herself back out of his arms.

He simply gathered her closer and held on tight.

"This doesn't happen with anyone else," she sniffed, resigning herself to being held captive in his arms. "I don't shout at people. I don't throw things. I don't get mad or cry or—" she flashed a vengeful look at him from under her damp lashes "—or go around wanting to tear another woman's hair out by the roots. I'm a nice, normal sane woman."

"America's sweetheart," Zeke agreed, laughter lurking in his voice.

"Yes! No! Oh, I don't know anymore." She bounced her curled fist off his shoulder. "It's not funny, Zeke. I'm dead serious about this. Ever since you came back into my life, I just don't know who I am anymore."

"And it scares you, not knowing."

"Yes. It terrifies me. I'm afraid that . . . that I'll . . ."

"You're afraid you'll what?"

"I'm afraid I'll lose myself again, like the last time. I fell completely apart when you— Oh, I know you didn't betray me. I believe that. I do. But I thought you had and it . . . it broke something inside me. I didn't know who I was and I didn't care. Not about myself. Not about anything. I hate to admit this now, but I wanted to die, back then."

"Ariel, sweetheart. I—"

"I know it's horrible. But it's the truth. It wasn't until the first time Cameron moved inside me that I started to care again. Don't you see, Zeke? Back then, I had Cameron to give me strength and keep me going. But she has her own life now. I won't have her this time, not like I did before."

"You won't need Cameron this time," Zeke said. "You have me." He touched her cheek gently, reverently, willing her to believe. And to trust. "You have us."

Her gaze locked with his, full of hope and yearning and the desire to believe it would all work out all right this time. "Truly?"

"Truly," he vowed. "We're not those two kids who were too insecure and stupid and afraid to fight for each other and what they had. Those two kids didn't even know that what they had together was *worth* fighting for. We do." He cupped her face in his hands and stared deeply into her eyes. "Don't we, Ariel?" he pleaded.

She stared up into his eyes for a long moment, her gaze searching, hopeful, serious. "Yes," she said, knowing, finally, that it was true. What they had was worth anything. "Yes, we do."

He kissed her then—they kissed each other—a soft, sweet, solemn, thankful kiss that left both of them smiling.

"And we'll love each other forever," he murmured against her lips, needing to hear her say it.

"Forever," she agreed fervently.

"And we'll be there for each other."

"Always."

"And we'll trust each other."

"Implicitly," she said, without a flicker of doubt or hesitation.

"And we'll... What?" he asked, feeling her smile against his mouth.

"I'll trust you," she said teasingly, feeling secure enough to joke about it. "But I can't promise I won't snatch some poor woman bald-headed for looking at you crosswise."

With a joyous shout of laughter, Zeke scooped her up in his arms and laid her on the bed. "Your image will never be the same."

* * * * *

COMING UP IN BACHELOR ARMS

Next month, don't miss PASSION AND SCANDAL (October 1995, #557), the third and final steamy story by bestselling Candace Schuler in Temptation's exciting Bachelor Arms miniseries. Willow Ryan puts Steve Hart's investigative skills—and his feelings for her—to the ultimate test when she stirs up danger at

*Bachelor Arms in search of her father's true
identity.
Next to move into Bachelor Arms are the
heroes and heroines in books by ever-popular
Judith Arnold.*

URBAN COWBOYS

A Stetson and spurs don't make a man a cowboy.

Being a real cowboy means being able to tough it out on the ranch and on the range. Three Manhattan city slickers with something to prove meet that challenge…and succeed.

But are they man enough to handle the three wild western women who lasso their hearts?

Bestselling author Vicki Lewis Thompson will take you on the most exciting trail ride of your life with her fabulous new trilogy—Urban Cowboys.

THE TRAILBLAZER #555 (September 1995)

THE DRIFTER #559 (October 1995)

THE LAWMAN #563 (November 1995)

Do you have a secret fantasy?

Researcher Eva Campbell does. She's an expert on virtual reality and in her computer she's created the perfect man. Except her fantasy lover is much more real than she could ever imagine.... Experience love with the ideal man in Mallory Rush's #558 KISS OF THE BEAST, available in October.

Everybody has a secret fantasy. And you'll find them all in Temptation's exciting new yearlong miniseries, Secret Fantasies. Throughout 1995 one book each month focuses on the hero or heroine's innermost romantic desires....

HARLEQUIN® *Temptation*

BACHELOR ARMS SURVEY

TALES OF TRANSFORMATION!
From Confirmed Bachelors to Super Suitors!

What is the best way to land a bachelor?

1. Home Cooking—the way to every man's heart

2. Jealousy—set loose the green-eyed monster

3. Temptation—dress for success

4. Game Playing—ignore him, feign indifference

5. Role Reversal—romance *him* for a change

6. Be Frugal—move in together to save money;
    once you've got him, don't let go

We want to hear from you, so please send in your
responses to:

> In the U.S.: BACHELOR ARMS,
> P.O. Box 9076, Buffalo, NY 14269-9076

> In Canada: BACHELOR ARMS,
> P.O. Box 637, Ft. Erie, ON L2A 5X3

Name: _____

Address:_____ City:_____

State/Prov.: _____ Zip/Postal Code:_____

Please note that all entries become the property of
Harlequin and we may publish them in any publication,
with credit at our discretion.

OFFICIAL RULES

FLYAWAY VACATION SWEEPSTAKES 3449

NO PURCHASE OR OBLIGATION NECESSARY

Three Harlequin Reader Service 1995 shipments will contain respectively, coupons for entry into three different prize drawings, one for a trip for two to San Francisco, another for a trip for two to Las Vegas and the third for a trip for two to Orlando, Florida. To enter any drawing using an Entry Coupon, simply complete and mail according to directions.

There is no obligation to continue using the Reader Service to enter and be eligible for any prize drawing. You may also enter any drawing by hand printing the words "Flyaway Vacation," your name and address on a 3"x5" card and the destination of the prize you wish that entry to be considered for (i.e., San Francisco trip, Las Vegas trip or Orlando trip). Send your 3"x5" entries via first-class mail (limit: one entry per envelope) to: Flyaway Vacation Sweepstakes 3449, c/o Prize Destination you wish that entry to be considered for, P.O. Box 1315, Buffalo, NY 14269-1315, USA or P.O. Box 610, Fort Erie, Ontario L2A 5X3, Canada.

To be eligible for the San Francisco trip, entries must be received by 5/30/95; for the Las Vegas trip, 7/30/95; and for the Orlando trip, 9/30/95.

Winners will be determined in random drawings conducted under the supervision of D.L. Blair, Inc., an independent judging organization whose decisions are final, from among all eligible entries received for that drawing. San Francisco trip prize includes round-trip airfare for two, 4-day/3-night weekend accommodations at a first-class hotel, and $500 in cash (trip must be taken between 7/30/95—7/30/96, approximate prize value—$3,500); Las Vegas trip includes round-trip airfare for two, 4-day/3-night weekend accommodations at a first-class hotel, and $500 in cash (trip must be taken between 9/30/95—9/30/96, approximate prize value—$3,500); Orlando trip includes round-trip airfare for two, 4-day/3-night weekend accommodations at a first-class hotel, and $500 in cash (trip must be taken between 11/30/95—11/30/96, approximate prize value—$3,500). All travelers must sign and return a Release of Liability prior to travel. Hotel accommodations and flights are subject to accommodation and schedule availability. Sweepstakes open to residents of the U.S. (except Puerto Rico) and Canada, 18 years of age or older. Employees and immediate family members of Harlequin Enterprises, Ltd., D.L. Blair, Inc., their affiliates, subsidiaries and all other agencies, entities and persons connected with the use, marketing or conduct of this sweepstakes are not eligible. Odds of winning a prize are dependent upon the number of eligible entries received for that drawing. Prize drawing and winner notification for each drawing will occur no later than 15 days after deadline for entry eligibility for that drawing. Limit: one prize to an individual, family or organization. All applicable laws and regulations apply. Sweepstakes offer void wherever prohibited by law. Any litigation within the province of Quebec respecting the conduct and awarding of the prizes in this sweepstakes must be submitted to the Regies des loteries et Courses du Quebec. In order to win a prize, residents of Canada will be required to correctly answer a time-limited arithmetical skill-testing question. Value of prizes are in U.S. currency.

Winners will be obligated to sign and return an Affidavit of Eligibility within 30 days of notification. In the event of noncompliance within this time period, prize may not be awarded. If any prize or prize notification is returned as undeliverable, that prize will not be awarded. By acceptance of a prize, winner consents to use of his/her name, photograph or other likeness for purposes of advertising, trade and promotion on behalf of Harlequin Enterprises, Ltd., without further compensation, unless prohibited by law.

For the names of prizewinners (available after 12/31/95), send a self-addressed, stamped envelope to: Flyaway Vacation Sweepstakes 3449 Winners, P.O. Box 4200, Blair, NE 68009.

RVC KAL